P9-CKN-517

THE BASIC LAWS OF ARITHMETIC

GOTTLOB FREGE

THE BASIC LAWS OF ARITHMETIC

Exposition of the System

Translated and Edited,
with an Introduction,
by MONTGOMERY FURTH

UNIVERSITY OF CALIFORNIA PRESS
Berkeley and Los Angeles 1964

University of California Press
Berkeley and Los Angeles, California

Cambridge University Press
London, England

©1964 by The Regents of the University of California
Library of Congress Catalog Card Number: 64-23479

Manufactured in the United States of America

EDITOR'S INTRODUCTION

1

The publication in 1893 of the first volume of Gottlob Frege's *Grundgesetze der Arithmetik* is now widely regarded as a landmark in the history of thought; yet in retrospect it appears in a light rather different from that in which Frege himself viewed it.

To Frege it was the culmination of the work of half a lifetime, intended to afford a rigorous and detailed substantiation of the view (later known as 'logicism') that the content expressed by true propositions of arithmetic and analysis is not something of an irreducibly mathematical character, nor synthetic *a priori* as Kant had held, nor again empirical in nature as J. S. Mill had held, but to the contrary, such propositions express truths of pure logic. Frege had broached this thesis in his *Grundlagen der Arithmetik*[2] of 1884 for the case of the cardinal numbers, together with elaborate discussion and criticism of rival views and an attempt at a nontechnical philosophical justification of Frege's approach to the foundations of his subject. The criticisms were lethal and the justification imposing, but Frege was aware that even this did not place his view beyond all doubt. Three further things were required:

(1) we must actually set out a (preferably small) number of assertions which, when their meaning was explained, would be indisputably recognized as expressing truths of pure logic;

(2) we must actually set out a (preferably small) number of principles which, when their manner of use was explained, would be indisputably recognized as sound rules of inference, in the sense that, applied to logically true premisses, the transformations

---

[1]This Introduction is intended chiefly for students and others to whom the study of Frege is new, though the connoisseur may find occasional points of interest.

[2]Bibliographical information relating to writings of Frege referred to in this Introduction is given on pp. lviii ff.

permitted by these principles could not issue in any but logically true conclusions; and

(3) we must then actually produce derivations of the standard propositions of arithmetic and analysis from our propositions of logic (and no other propositions), using our principles of inference (and no other principles).

This threefold task was to be carried out in *Grundgesetze*. For Frege the paramount part of this task was (3); by far the bulk of his book was devoted to it, and it was in terms of the success or failure of (3) that he thought of the success or failure of the book as a whole—as was natural, given his purpose of vindicating 'logicism' by actual demonstration.

For us today, on the other hand, the greater value belongs to Frege's handling of (1) and (2). There are several reasons for this. One is that Frege's investigations of the concepts of logical truth and of logical consequence, undertaken in the course of meeting (1) and (2), amounted to the creation single-handed of the subject of mathematical logic as later understood[3], issuing in a formal system of logic incorporating propositional calculus, first- and second-order quantification theory, and a theory of sets developed within second-order quantification theory. The influence of Frege's formulations upon subsequent developments has been somewhat indirect. At first they were ignored, like the rest of his work. In 1902 they came to the attention of Russell, who by that date had arrived at certain similar ideas independently, and their effect can be discerned to a degree in the system of Whitehead and Russell's *Principia Mathematica*. But it was *Principia* and not *Grundgesetze* that became the foundation for work in logic thereafter; Frege's logical ideas again fell into comparative neglect, and to this date are generally only superficially understood where they differ from those of *Principia*. Yet these ideas abound in both subtlety and power; further, Frege's presentation is carried out in accordance with standards of definiteness, clarity, and rigor far higher than those prevailing in *Principia*—standards that were not reattained for many years thereafter.

There is a second, related reason for attaching great importance today to Frege's treatment of (1) and (2): that is, Frege's

---

[3]It should be noted that several of the technical innovations actually date back to Frege's early book *Begriffsschrift* of 1879.

explanation of the primitive basis of his system of logic, and particularly of the primitive symbolism, is undertaken in terms of a deeply thought-out semantical interpretation, which in turn embodies an entire philosophy of language. The influence of the latter upon the semantical structure and even the syntax of the language developed makes itself felt steadily throughout the discussion. This philosophy of language is very profound, and possesses great interest quite independent of its origin as the handmaiden of 'logicism'. It too is not generally well understood even today.

A third point is that the project of the book, regarded as Frege regarded it, was a failure, for the set theory of his system is inconsistent, and yet is indispensable for the derivation of propositions of mathematics. The inconsistency, which became known to Frege through a letter from Russell in the summer of 1902 while the second volume of *Grundgesetze* was in press, renders it quite impossible that 'logicism' be substantiated by the system in even essentially its present form. And subsequent work dealing with the relations between logic and mathematics has in any case now far outstripped the contribution of *Grundgesetze* to that subject.

Let us dwell for another moment on the relevance of Frege's work to present-day philosophical interests. In recent decades of this century within the movement broadly termed 'analytical philosophy' a division has occurred between two approaches to the general topic of meaning. One approach, much the older, finds the vehicle of meaning in the linguistic *expression*; the other, more recent, is based rather on looking to the *use* or occasions of the use of expressions. The first approach is based on the ancient metaphysical tradition that views phenomena of meaning in the form of relations holding between language and the world; characteristic is its investigation of these phenomena in the context of a formalized language, where the results of enquiry take the form of semantical metatheorems. (This is not new, but as old as Plato; certain methods are new.) The second approach views phenomena of meaning in terms of the great variety of *acts* that may be performed by speakers of a language in the everyday contexts of its use; accordingly natural rather than formalized languages are enquired into, and the idea of 'relations between language and the world' as a setting for philosophical investigation is held to be a source of confusion. Proponents of the first approach derogate the second as imprecise, unscientific, and willfully or ignorantly shirking the tools of modern logic. Proponents of the second approach derogate the first for its oversimplifying of the richness and multiplicity of language, for studying idealized abstract structures instead of language as it is, and for hypostatizing meanings.

It is a misfortune, though perhaps inevitable, that this division has presented itself as a conflict, since the approaches are obviously complementary and rivalry has obstructed fruitful investigation of their mutual relations. The importance of Frege's work, which falls squarely within the first approach, is simply this: the theory of meaning it presents is more subtle and more complex than any other such theory of its kind, subtle and complex in ways that have not been taken into account in attacks either upon it or upon better known theories falling within the same category. The point is not that this theory should therefore be acknowledged as carrying the day for the first approach, but that a thorough understanding of it may help to form a basis upon which we might hope to penetrate the problems that the two approaches face in common.

Thus Frege's book, viewed as he viewed it, is chiefly of historical interest—though the chapter of history it constitutes is a great one. Viewed from a modern standpoint, however, it is well worth study in its own right by philosophers as well as logicians and historians of thought, and it is in this spirit that the present translation of its philosophically and logically most important portions is offered.

In what follows I give first a rapid and superficial description of the course of developments in the parts here translated, then comment somewhat more fully on certain points of particular importance, and finally offer some notes to the translation itself.

2

The present work is a translation of approximately one-fifth of *Grundgesetze der Arithmetik*, consisting of the introductory portions of the first volume and an epilogue appended to the second (Appendix II, below). It falls into three parts.

First is Frege's Introduction to the first volume, outlining the book and its aims, and distinguishing its standpoint from the then current 'formalism' in mathematics[4] and 'psychologism' in logic. The treatment of the latter turns into a long and rather violent polemic against Erdmann's *Logik*[5]; one gathers that the appearance of this book in 1892 on the eve of the publication of *Grundgesetze* had exasperated Frege beyond endurance. It should perhaps be remembered that Frege had some cause for bitterness in the complacent misunderstanding and lack of appreciation accorded his earlier works, where indeed they were noticed at all; and no doubt he was right in laying a large part of the blame upon fashionable 'psychologizing' tendencies among contemporary logicians. However this may be, the Foreword is useful in conveying an idea of the role that the book was intended to play and the prevailing situation in which it was to play it, at least as these appeared to Frege.

The second and chief part is the "Exposition of the Begriffsschrift", a compressed but extremely thorough exposition of the formalized language in which the later reasoning of *Grundgesetze* is carried out, together with informal justifications of the propositions to be adopted as axioms ('Basic Laws') without proof, and of the rules of inference to be employed in generating new propositions from the axioms.

The "Exposition" begins with a brief survey of the kinds of entities comprising the logical universe of the book: *functions*, including concepts and relations[6], and *objects*, including truth-values, courses-of-values and the extensions of concepts. Then we turn to the system itself: names of truth-values are first distinguished from asserted propositions, and then names of various functions are introduced that are later to be used in forming complex names of truth-values (as well as of other objects), and

---

[4]This is not the later 'formalism' of Hilbert, a program of seeking metamathematical consistency proofs for classical mathematics, but a view ascribing to classical mathematics itself the *intrinsic* character of being a 'game' played by manipulating symbols on paper. Frege might have put the difference thus: the procedure of the later (Hilbertian) formalist cannot be described without distinguishing between the use and the mention of mathematical expressions; the view of the earlier derives from confusing them.

[5]Benno Erdmann, *Logik*. Band I. *Logische Elementarlehre* (Halle a/S.: Max Niemeyer, 1892).

[6]"Relation" is always understood to mean *binary* relation.

thereby in asserted propositions. These function-names correspond more or less closely to the modern truth-functional connectives of negation and the conditional, also the identity-sign and the (first-order) quantifiers[7], a notation for courses-of-values and what corresponds to an operation-symbol for forming definite descriptions. But here it must be borne in mind that for Frege the negation- and conditional-signs, for example, are in fact not connectives—in the sense in which a connective is a syncategorematic expression or 'improper symbol' not itself having denotation—but *names* denoting certain functions. Not only are they so called, but they are regarded as replaceable by variables, which for a syncategorematic expression is impossible. The same applies to the definite-description sign, which is not literally an operation-symbol but a function-name. All of these signs are explained informally in accordance with the semantical viewpoint of the book, accompanied by many examples.

Next we encounter transformation-rules, regarded as permitting transitions from one asserted proposition (not: name of a truth-value) to another. For sentential logic these answer roughly to Modus Ponens, Hypothetical Syllogism, Contraposition, and a rule for which there is no title in general use but which might be called 'Concentration of Antecedents'. For predicate logic there is a rule of Universal Generalization. (Rules of substitution and of alphabetic change of bound variable are laid down later, in the Summary of the Rules.) Axioms ('Basic Laws') are laid down, whose nearest equivalents in more recent notation would be

$$p \rightarrow (q \rightarrow p) \qquad \text{(Basic Law I)}$$
$$\sim(p \leftrightarrow \sim q) \rightarrow (p \leftrightarrow q) \qquad \text{(Basic Law IV)}$$
$$y = (\imath x)(y = x) \qquad \text{(Basic Law VI)}$$
$$(x)f(x) \rightarrow f(y) \qquad \text{(Basic Law IIa)}.$$

Care must be taken lest these approximations mislead. For example, the range of the variables in Basic Laws I and IV is not confined to truth-values, but extends over all objects whatever; accordingly the constants eligible to replace them are not merely sentences (names of truth-values) but names of any objects. Thus, for example,

"the Parthenon $\rightarrow$ ($2 + 2 = 4 \rightarrow$ the Parthenon)"

---

[7]Described as names of second-level functions. Cf. 4 below.

(assuming the constituent names to be (denoting) proper names of the language) would be a legitimate instance of Basic Law I. Again, since sentences are regarded as names denoting truth-values, Frege has no need for the biconditional sign used above, the identity-sign being available.

Next, function-names of a new kind[8] are introduced corresponding to second-order quantifiers, and further Basic Laws are laid down. One,

$$g(x = y) \to g[(f)(f(y) \to f(x))], \quad \text{(Basic Law III)}$$

has as one instance the proposition

$$(x = y) \to (f)(f(y) \to f(x)),$$

sometimes called the Principle of Indiscernibility of Identicals, and as another instance (taking "g" as "not"),

$$\sim(x = y) \to \sim(f)(f(y) \to f(x)),$$

Leibniz' law of Identity of Indiscernibles. A second Basic Law in which figures the idea of second-order quantification is

$$(f)G(f) \to G(g),[9] \quad \text{(Basic Law IIb)}$$

placing the same condition of instantiability upon universally quantified function-variables as does Basic Law IIa for object-variables.

Also introduced is the ill-starred Basic Law V on the notion of the *course-of-values of a function*, a special case being the notion of the *extension of a concept*: notions that for present heuristic purposes we may identify with those respectively of a function-in-extension and of a class [10]. This Basic Law asserts that for two functions to determine the same course-of-values it is necessary and sufficient that they have always the same value for the same argument. For the special case of concepts, it asserts that for two concepts to determine the same extension (or class) it is necessary and sufficient that precisely the same objects fall under each, or

$$\hat{x}f(x) = \hat{x}g(x) \leftrightarrow (x)(f(x) \leftrightarrow g(x)) \quad \text{(Basic Law V)}.$$

This concludes the exposition of the primitive basis of the system. The next step is to devise methods of abbreviating complex names by definition. We are first given an elegant review of the semantical position, followed by the rules to be

---

[8] Described as names of third-level functions. Cf. **4** below.

[9] Here my makeshift modern notation is exceptionally inaccurate; cf. **4**.

[10] Cf. **6** below.

observed in introducing such abbreviations. There follow definitions of the several particular functions, concepts, and objects that are to be used in the earliest constructions of the book: these include the many-oneness of a relation, the converse of a relation, the cardinality ('Number') of the extension of a concept, the particular cardinal numbers zero and one, the relation of immediate succession in the series of finite cardinals, and the proper and improper ancestral of a relation. (Many further definitions are given in the course of later developments.)

Finally, the Basic Laws are collected, the Rules are stated in final and comprehensive form, and numerous immediate corollaries are derived by the Rules from the Basic Laws.

With this the "Exposition of the Begriffsschrift" is complete. However, a third part has been added in the present book: two Appendices containing material pertinent to the fact that the system as it stands is inconsistent. The offending principle is of course Basic Law V, about which Frege himself confessed some uneasiness from the beginning[11]. More accurately, the inconsistency arises from the simultaneous maintaining of two theses: (1) that to every first-level concept there answers a certain object standing to it as its extension, whose identity-condition is that provided in Basic Law V, and (2) that this object is a full-fledged or 'proper' (*eigentlich*) object, meaning that it is an admissible argument for every first-level function whatever. Basic Law V, so interpreted, enables us to derive within the system the antinomy that has become known as Russell's Paradox. The derivation, together with a discussion of the crisis and Frege's attempt to repair the system, is given here as Appendix II; it was written by Frege in the few months following receipt of the shattering letter from Russell announcing the inconsistency, and was appended to the second volume of *Grundgesetze*. Even to the modern reader, beneficiary of intensive subsequent discussion of such matters, the inconsistency may not be instantly apparent by inspection of Basic Law V; but it becomes quite patent when we learn that this Law implies a theorem whose modern approximation for the case of concepts is

$$f(y) \leftrightarrow y \in \hat{x}f(x)$$

without limitation on y or f; the latter is indeed the first theorem

---

[11]Cf. his Introduction, pp. 3-4 below.

proved in *Grundgesetze* after the "Exposition". It yields Russell's Paradox immediately upon substitution of "$\backsim((\;\;) \; \epsilon \; (\;\;))$" for "$f(\;\;)$" and of "$\hat{x}(\backsim(x \; \epsilon \; x))$" for "$y$". Since this theorem figures in Frege's discussion of the inconsistency, and its derivation can be understood in the light of the "Exposition" alone, the derivation has been included as Appendix I.

3

Certain points must be clear if the theory of the book is to be understood; since some of these are not fully explained in the book itself, and others seem to be easily misunderstood, some discussion is called for. They are conveniently arranged under the head of five distinctions: (1) sense and denotation, (2) function and object, (3) name and mark, (4) function and course-of-values, (5) name (or mark) of a truth-value and assertion.

Because these distinctions cut across one another in various ways it is not possible to treat each in total isolation; hence some matters may be touched on earlier that cannot be understood fully until later. But it is of great importance to see from the beginning that the first two distinctions are quite independent of each other: the first distinction divides the *denotation* (*Bedeutung*) of a simple or complex name from its *sense* (*Sinn*); the second divides the denotations and the senses of all names into *functions*, described as 'unsaturated' or 'in need of completion' (*ungesättigt, ergänzungsbedürftig*), and *objects,* described as 'saturated' and 'self-subsistent' (*gesättigt, selbstständig*).

In order to explain this and proceed, let us adopt a few elementary quasi-technical terms. First, let us use the term "complete name" to describe an expression that either names or purports to name a determinate object. Thus proper names in the ordinary sense would be complete names in our sense: names such as "Napoleon Bonaparte", "the Schneekoppe", "Venus" (taken as naming a planet), and also proper names that, although not (as far as we know) names of any object, still purport to name some object, such as "Nessus", which purports to name a certain centaur, and "Nausicaa", which purports to name a young woman, and "Venus" taken as naming a goddess. Let us also for the sake of argument admit Arabic numerals as complete names in our sense, such as "9", thus imagining that the number 9 is a certain determinate object, though an abstract object.

Next, let us enrich the category of complete names by distinguishing between simple and complex complete names, understanding by a complex complete name a complete name having a complete name as a proper part. Thus "Napoleon Bonaparte" is a simple complete name, but "the elder brother of Napoleon Bonaparte" is a complex complete name which names Joseph Bonaparte. "9" is a simple complete name, but "9^2" is a complex complete name which names the number 81; "3^2" is a complex complete name which, like "9", names 9. "The shirt of Nessus" is a complex complete name which (as far as we know) does not name anything.

Thus enriched, the category of complete names now includes some expressions that might not be regarded as proper names in the ordinary sense, but the notion of complete name still has a straightforward intuitive content. Shortly we shall have to extend both our notion of a complete name in general, and later (in a somewhat different direction) our notion of complex complete name in particular; for the moment, however, they will serve us. What we are calling a complete name, Frege calls a proper name (*Eigenname*).

Next, let us call what is left over when one or more complete names are removed from a complex complete name, an *incomplete expression*, and let us for convenience mark the gap (or gaps) thus left with open parentheses. Accordingly, "the elder brother of ( )", "( )^2", "the shirt of ( )", and so on, will be incomplete expressions. Our later extension of the notion of complex complete name will require us also to extend our notion of incomplete expression; but for the moment it will serve us.

Now let us return to Frege. Where we have used the words "is a name of" or "names" to describe a relation between a complete name and a certain object, Frege uses the term "*denotes*" (*bedeutet*), and speaks of the object named by the name as the *denotation* (*Bedeutung*) of the name. But furthermore, for Frege an incomplete expression, as we have called it, is also a name, and is also conceived as capable of denoting something, or of having denotation; its denotation, however, is said to be not an *object* (as for complete names) but a *function*. Now this (unlike the use of "complete name" rather than "proper name") is not a mere matter of terminology but an extremely important and controversial part of the theory; hence to evoke this part of Frege's view we shall now speak of such expressions as "( )^2" and "the shirt of ( )" as *incomplete names* instead of incomplete expressions (Frege's term is "function-name"). As we said, then, objects, which are denoted by complete names, are 'saturated', and functions, which are denoted by incomplete names, are 'unsaturated'.

It will be useful to adopt as a convention the practice of using the terms "complete" and "incomplete" only to apply to expressions, and confine the use of "saturated" and "unsaturated" to the denotations[12] of expressions, although Frege uses the two pairs of terms more or less convertibly. (But our convention is purely terminological; Frege does not, as is sometimes thought, *confuse* his use of (e.g.) "unsaturated" for expressions with his use of it for the denotations of these expressions, although he does sometimes tend to exaggerate the resemblance between them.)

What must be clearly understood at the outset is that when Frege speaks of functions as the denotations of incomplete names, he is using the word "denotation" (i.e., *"Bedeutung"*) in a manner that is as precisely analogous to his use of it in connection with complete names as is permitted by the fact that functions are supposed to be 'unsaturated' whereas objects are not; his use of the word "name" itself is *pari passu* as literal in the one case as in the other. This must be stressed because of an idea current in the literature that Frege uses *"Bedeutung"* in the case of incomplete names not for a technical notion of denotation but rather for some undifferentiated notion of 'meaning', or again that he uses it in that case for something like what he calls "sense" in the case of complete names. This idea cannot withstand thorough exposure to Frege's writings[13]. Of course, we are still in the dark as to what is meant by the assertion that incomplete names have a denotation (*Bedeutung*) that is *'unsaturated'*; the point is that we shall be poorly placed to understand this if we suppose that in it by *"Bedeutung"* Frege does not mean denotation at all.

On the basis, then, that the first two distinctions are mutually independent, a point expressible by saying that complete names

---

[12] And, later, the senses of expressions.

[13] Cf., in the present work, §§29-31 (pp. 84-89 below).

are thought to have saturated senses and saturated denotations (i.e., objects) and incomplete names are thought to have unsaturated senses and unsaturated denotations (i.e., functions), let us consider the sense-denotation distinction.

Sense and denotation. Frege's earliest and most detailed account of this distinction, that of "Über Sinn und Bedeutung" in 1892, is explicitly confined to the case of complete names[14], a fact perhaps partially responsible for the mistaken view that the distinction is not intended to apply to incomplete names also. Its application to incomplete names is better deferred to our discussion of them in **4** below. For complete names then, the proposal is that such a name, whether simple or complex, be thought of as possessing over and above its denotation (if any) a further component or type of meaning called its sense. The notion of sense corresponds perhaps more closely than that of denotation to our ordinary notion of 'meaning', in that it comprises, not the object named by a name, but something more like what we *understand* by the name: perhaps that which, if we have grasped it, enables us to say of any object after appropriately thorough investigation whether or not it *is* the denotation of the name. However this may be, Frege is emphatic that the sense of a name is not to be identified with the ideas or images that may be associated with or evoked by the name in any mind or minds; it is *objective*, existing independent of anyone's in fact having grasped it, and of there being in fact any name whose sense it is. As a name is said to *denote* its denotation (if it has a denotation), so it is said to *express* its sense; and clearly it is possible for a name devoid of denotation to express a sense. (For example, let us agree that the name "Nessus", though denotationless, expresses a sense, and that this sense is identical with that expressed by the name "most knavish centaur".) On the other hand, apparently it is ruled out that a name might denote a denotation without expressing a sense; thus no complete name is simply an 'unmeaning mark' or 'logically proper name' in the sense of its meaning being wholly exhausted by its denotation. Although the last may seem to prejudge a traditional topic for philosophical quarrels, in the present connection this is not of very great importance; for the plausibility of an 'unmeaning mark' view of complete names is

---

[14]"Über Sinn und Bedeutung," p. 27.

largely confined to simple complete names, whereas the decisive applications of sense-denotation theory occur where the names in question are complex[15].

That is, the denotation of a complex name is invariably a function of the denotations of its constituent names, and the sense of a complex name is invariably a function of the senses of its constituent names; these might be called the Basic Principles of sense and denotation, upon which rest the corresponding principles of interchange: replacement of a constituent name in a complex name by a name having the same denotation leaves the denotation of the whole unchanged; and replacement of a constituent name in a complex name by a name having the same sense leaves the sense of the whole unchanged.

Formally, what distinguishes sense from denotation—besides the provision that a name may possess the former and lack the latter but not conversely—is that two complex names denoting the same denotation may still express different senses, although the converse cannot obtain. Thus the theory renders the relation of sameness of sense between names as subject to some stricter or narrower criterion than that for sameness of denotation. Frege does not explain in "Über Sinn und Bedeutung" or elsewhere what degree of additional strictness he would conceive as appropriate (he would say, as correct), nor, apparently, did he attempt to formulate the various *prima facie* possible alternatives. The weakest of these, as well as the most easily developed, would construe the names "A" and "B" as coinciding in sense just in case "$A = B$" was not merely true but necessary or logically valid[16]; but it is worth observing that Frege's intuitive criterion is at any rate considerably more severe than this. For example, by his logicistic view of arithmetical truths such a statement as "$2^2 = 2+2$" is logically valid; yet he holds that "2^2" and "$2+2$" do not express the same sense[17].

The reasons for making such a distinction and publishing an

---

[15] It is worth remarking that in *Grundgesetze* there are no simple complete names at all.

[16] This alternative is that called Alternative (2) in Church's "A Formulation of the Logic of Sense and Denotation" (Henle, Kallen and Langer, eds., *Structure, Method and Meaning: Essays in honor of Henry M. Sheffer*, New York, 1951).

[17] Cf. pp. 6 (note 3), 35, below.

account of it prior to the appearance of *Grundgesetze* were two-fold. So far as *sense* is concerned the motivation was for the most part negative, by way of setting it aside: and indeed in the book once the distinction has been made, except for scattered elucidatory remarks and the doctrine of *assertion*[18] the entire development is on the level of denotation. The interpretation intended for the system is wholly extensional; the distinction enabled this to be brought out and intensional aspects of meaning to be kept from obtruding. But in addition to this general motivation there were two quite specific problems that had had to be solved in the course of constructing the system and whose solution was obtained by means of the distinction. One was that of securing a satisfactory account of identity; the other was to establish the point expressed in terms of the distinction by saying that sentences are complete names having truth-values as denotation.

In Frege's early work *Begriffsschrift*, identity had been handled as a relation between expressions; namely,

$$``A \equiv B"$$

was to express the circumstance of the sign "A" and the sign "B" standing in the relation of 'equality of content' (*Inhaltsgleichheit*). Thus the signs of the language acquired a split signification (*Zwiespältigkeit in der Bedeutung*); where they did not occur to the right or left of the sign "$\equiv$" they were to be taken as 'standing for' or 'representing' their 'content', but where they did so occur, they were thought to stand for themselves. "Content" was used for some undifferentiated notion of 'meaning'; but at least in this connection we can take it as amounting to the same as "denotation". The reason for so regarding identity seems to have been this: if we took "$A = B$" as expressing a relation between the denotation of "A" and the denotation of "B" (i.e., between A and B), then since "$A = B$" is true if and only if the denotation of "A" and the denotation of "B" are the same object, it appears that the relation expressed could only be the relation borne by an object to and only to *itself*. Now indeed identity is precisely such a relation; yet if this is the end of the matter it becomes very difficult to explain the difference between "$A = B$" and "$A = A$" when

---

[18] Cf. **7** below.

"$A = B$" is true, to account for the obvious fact that true statements of the form "$A = B$" may constitute important and interesting extensions of our knowledge whereas statements of the form "$A = A$" do not. The only way out, so long as we proceed on the basis that names have only denotation (or 'content'), is to read "$A = B$" not as expressing the relation of identity between A and B (i.e., for true "$A = B$", between A and A), but rather as expressing the relation of having-the-same-denotation between "A" and "B". This was the reading adopted in *Begriffsschrift*. It has the merit of accounting for the interest of true "$A = B$" as against the uninformativeness of "$A = A$". But the price is exorbitantly high, for the device renders it practically impossible to integrate the theory of identity into the formalized object-language itself; e.g., to state generally such a law as that if $F(a)$ and $a = b$ then $F(b)$.

By adoption of the sense-denotation distinction, this situation is completely resolved in *Grundgesetze*. A name invariably denotes its ordinary denotation, whether it occurs as a limb of an identity-sentence or not, and it becomes possible to explain the circumstance that is asserted to obtain by a statement of the form "$A = B$" without becoming entangled in the difficulties encountered above. Here it will be convenient to adopt another terminological convention, one that will also serve us in **7** when we consider the relation between a name of a truth-value and an assertion. That is: given a name expressing a sense and denoting a denotation, a certain relation holds between that sense and that denotation, a relation for which Frege has no word; let us say that the sense *is a sense of* that denotation and that the denotation *has* that sense *as a sense*. (To avoid ambiguity, therefore, henceforth I shall never speak of a sense as 'the sense of' an expression, but only as the sense *expressed by* an expression, and I shall never speak of an expression's 'having' a sense, but only of its *expressing* a sense. [19]) On this basis,

---

[19] 'Being a sense of' as used here answers to Church's 'being a concept of', where 'anything which is capable of being the sense of [= expressed by] a name of x is called a *concept* of x' (*op. cit.*, p. 11; cf. also Church's *Introduction to Mathematical Logic* [Princeton, 1956], Vol. I, p. 6). Since we are reserving the word "concept" to translate Frege's "*Begriff*", this otherwise unexceptionable idiom is not available to us. (Frege occasionally speaks of senses 'belonging to' [*zugehören*] denotations; cf. "Über Sinn und Bedeutung," pp. 27, 35.)

then, what is asserted to obtain by a statement of the form "$A = B$" is that the sense expressed by "A" and the sense expressed by "B" are senses of the same denotation: a circumstance trivial where the senses expressed by "A" and "B" coincide (thus also for statements of the form "$A = A$") but capable of being interesting where they do not. Thus a threefold aim is attained: the signs in "$A = B$" denote the denotation(s) that they denote in other contexts, yet the difference in meaning between true "$A = B$" and "$A = A$" can be accounted for, yet the circumstance expressed by "$A = B$" is characterizable independently of the particular language in which the signs happen to occur. The aim achieved, a logic of identity could be developed and very heavily exploited within the system of *Grundgesetze*. Thus, then, one reason behind the distinction and the timing of the essay in which it was explained.

The other reason, perhaps even more important, concerns the construal of *sentences* as belonging to the category of complete names, and the truth-values (the True and the False) as their denotations; its importance is indicated by the fact that fully two-thirds of "Über Sinn und Bedeutung" is devoted to it. The overall structure of the reasoning is as follows. It is extremely natural to attempt to extend the principles of interchange, referred to earlier, to the case of sentences, and if we do so we obtain a striking parallel between the relation of a complete name and its denotation on the one hand, and the relation of a sentence and its truth-value on the other. Two aspects of this parallel are developed. (*a*) Just as, in the case of a complex complete name such as "the shirt of Nessus" or "the square of the largest finite number" that contains a denotationless part ("Nessus", "the largest finite number"), we regard the entire complex name as denotationless, so also, it is contended, in the case of a sentence such as "Nessus did not carry Deianeira across the river Evenus" or "the largest finite number is even" that contains a denotationless part, we regard the entire sentence as devoid of truth-value, as neither true nor false. (This contention is meant to describe our *ordinary* procedure.) (*b*) Just as replacement of a constituent denoting name in a complex complete name by a constituent name having the same denotation must necessarily leave the denotation of the whole unchanged (although the sense expressed by the whole may be altered), so also replacement of a constituent denoting name in a sentence by a constituent name having the same denotation must necessarily leave the truth-value of the sentence unchanged, although the resulting sentence may now contain [enthalten] a different thought [Gedanke].[20] Now of course this is not by itself conclusive; in any particular case much else might remain unchanged besides. But consistent application of the principle within a language of even moderate complexity leads inevitably to the conclusion that it is only the truth-value that *must* remain unchanged: 'What else could ever be found but the truth-value, that belongs quite generally to every sentence dealing with the denotation of its components and that remains unaltered by replacements of the kind in question?'[21]

Thus we find (*a*) that denotationless parts divest complex names of denotation and sentences of truth-value; (*b*) that the relation of any true sentence to its truth-value and of any false sentence to its truth-value is an exact parallel to the relation of any simple or complex name to its denotation. These parallels are very striking, but it should be observed that by themselves they would not *force* us to use the term ''denotes'' for both relations and accordingly admit sentences into the category of complete names. Why then do so? The reason is that doing so works a formidable simplification in the semantical theory governing the language, on several fronts. Frege desires to express laws of propositional logic by using variables, and these variables should be appropriately replaceable by sentences. The meaning of a variable is best explained by assigning it a range of possible values,[22] and then regarding constants substitutable for the variable as names denoting objects in this range. By admitting sentences into the category of complete names, we are able to treat sentential variables in the same way as those of other kinds, thus a sentence as denoting an object in the range of a sentential variable; otherwise we should have to

---

[20] A 'thought' being 'not the subjective performance of thinking but its objective content, which is capable of being the common property of many thinkers' (*ibid.*, p. 32, note).

[21] *Ibid.*, p. 35. Frege's own argument is rather sketchy at this point, but is easily supplemented. Cf. Church's review of Carnap's *Introduction to Semantics*, *Philosophical Review* 52 (1943), 298-304, and Church's *Introduction to Mathematical Logic*, Vol. I, pp. 24f.

[22] Cf. 5 below.

give some quite different account of the meaning of variables and the rationale of their replacement by constants, either in general or for the special case of sentential variables, and it is not easy to see what form this would take.

A different, and extremely important, consequence of regarding sentences as complete names is that it makes possible the explanation of the notions of a concept and a relation as special cases of the notion of a function, a topic to which we shall return in **4**.[23]

For such reasons as these, the construal of sentences as names is adopted to mark the parallels already discerned, and the parallels then force us to take the denotation of a sentence as its truth-value. (But because philosophical preconceptions surrounding the word "name" so easily cloud one's view of the matter, let it be stressed once again that the parallels would exist whether marked by the name-denotation terminology or not, and that so marking them evinces not a distorted or *outré* conception of *sentence*, but an unusually abstract and generalized conception of *name*.) A sentence has already been assumed to 'contain' a 'thought'; this notion is now incorporated into the theory not as the denotation of the sentence but as its *sense*; and accordingly the (studiedly vague) term "contain" is replaced by the technical term "express".

To the construal of sentences as complete names denoting truth-values there appear to be certain counterexamples that if not accounted for would force Frege either to abandon the construal or else to restrict drastically the scope of the principle of interchange for denotation. No such counterexamples occur in *Grundgesetze*, so that as far as the book itself was concerned he could stop here. But because they might undermine confidence in the general philosophical conceptions on which it rested, and perhaps because of their own interest, they are discussed in "Über Sinn und Bedeutung" and a manner of dealing

---

[23]It is sometimes thought that the fact that the notion of a concept and a relation can be construed as special cases of the notion of a function, provides an *argument* for regarding sentences as complete denoting names; but clearly this is back to front. The possibility of representing concept- and relation-words on the analogy of functional expressions depends entirely on complete sentences' *already* being thought of as having denotation in the same manner as functional expressions completed by a name of an argument.

with them is roughly sketched. The cases in point are of this type: the two sentences, e.g.,

(1)   "The blood circulates, traveling away from the heart through the arteries, and toward the heart through the veins"

and

(2)   "The heart is a muscle",

both being true, are supposed to have the same denotation; yet replacement of the first by the second in the true sentence

(3)   "Descartes was aware that the blood circulates, traveling away from the heart through the arteries, and toward the heart through the veins"

results in the false sentence

(4)   "Descartes was aware that the heart is a muscle",

suggesting that the truth of (1) and (2) may not guarantee them the same denotation, or alternatively that the denotation of a complex name is not invariably a function of the denotations of its constituent names. Both alternatives are unacceptable, the first for the reasons already set out, the second because it would amount to abandoning the basic principle of sense-denotation theory itself.

The answer of "Über Sinn und Bedeutung" is a doctrine of '*indirect* (or *oblique*) denotation' (*ungerade Bedeutung*), providing that in certain contexts, such as that following "Descartes was aware that", a sentence denotes not its *direct* (or *ordinary*) denotation (*gewöhnliche Bedeutung*), its truth-value, but instead its oblique denotation, identified with its ordinary sense: the thought which, outside such a context, it would express. Thus room is left for the difference of truth-value between (3) and (4), for what is relevant therein are the oblique denotations of (1) and (2), their ordinary senses, and these obviously differ. This saves the principle of interchange for denotation; the denotation of a complex name remains a function of the denotations of its constituent names; but certain complex names may contain parts generating contexts such that the denotations of constituent names within such contexts are their oblique rather than their ordinary denotations.

These problems can arise for complete names other than sentences, and can be handled in the same way. For example, the two names

(5)   "the number of major planets"
and
(6)   "9"

have the same denotation; yet replacement of the first by the second in the true sentence

(7)   "It is not necessary that the number of major planets be 9"

results in the false sentence

(8)   "It is not necessary that 9 be 9";

the response would be to rule "it is (not) necessary that" a context of the same kind as "Descartes was aware that", to declare the oblique (though not the ordinary) denotations of (5) and and (6) distinct, and proceed as before.

Suppose, following current practice, we term contexts of the kind in question 'oblique contexts'; the idea then is that if a language contains expressions generating oblique contexts, names capable of occurring in these are *ambiguous*; whether they denote their ordinary or their oblique denotations depends upon whether they occur in a nonoblique or an oblique context. Frege left the matter at this point, as he was entitled to do since oblique contexts were not to occur in *Grundgesetze*. If they had, he would have had to go further, in one or the other of two directions. He might have allowed the ambiguity to remain. This would require restrictions on the rules of inference; for example, so as to block the inference that otherwise would take us from (7) and

        "9 = the number of major planets"

to (8). On the other hand, a policy might be adopted of requiring that differences of denotation be reflected in differences of name, thus abolishing the ambiguity by employing, for example, some such expression as

                "$[9]_1$"

to denote the sense expressed by the expression "9". Thus "9" would invariably denote 9, that is, the number of major planets, but "$[9]_1$" would denote a certain sense of 9, namely $[9]_1$, something quite different from [the number of major planets]$_1$. (7) would be explicitly rewritten using the names "$[9]_1$" and "[the number of major planets]$_1$" and a new relation-word, asserting there to hold between the denotations of "$[9]_1$" and "[the number of major planets]$_1$" whatever relation it was that

(7) was previously regarded as asserting to hold between the senses ordinarily expressed (but in (7) obliquely denoted) by "9" and "the number of major planets". On this basis all contexts would be non-oblique and the rules of inference could remain mostly unmolested, but the formation rules would become much more complicated.

Since Frege left the matter where he did, it would take us beyond the scope of this Introduction to pursue further these two approaches to a logic of sense or intensions. There is not much to indicate which of them he would have adopted had he pressed further. On one hand, the evidence of "Über Sinn und Bedeutung" points in the direction of the first method; but on the other there is Frege's general policy of paralleling differences of semantical role by the use of distinct types of expression, as with complete versus incomplete names, and again with names versus marks, and again with names (and marks) of truth-values versus assertions: a policy that if invoked here would suggest the second method.

4

Function and object. Thus far we have considered the sense-denotation distinction only for the case of complete names (what Frege terms proper names), and this is Frege's procedure in "Über Sinn und Bedeutung". However, the distinction is also drawn for the other type of name: for *incomplete names* or, as Frege terms them, function-names. The denotation of a complete name is an object; that of an incomplete name is a *function*. Objects are 'saturated'; functions are '*unsaturated*'.

Frege also describes the sense expressed by an incomplete name as 'unsaturated',[24] and there is reason to believe that he held such a sense to be a 'function'[25]; however, nowhere in his writings does he *use* the word "function" for anything but the denotation of an incomplete name, and in this we shall follow him. As we have seen, he says little enough about the senses

---

[24] Cf. "Über Begriff und Gegenstand," p. 205; also the late series of essays "Der Gedanke," "Die Verneinung," and particularly "Gedankengefüge."

[25] Cf. H. Jackson, "Frege on Sense-Functions," *Analysis*, 23 (1962-1963), 84-87, in which unpublished material of Frege's is also adduced in favor of this view.

expressed by complete names, and scarcely anything at all is said of the senses expressed by incomplete names (save for their 'unsaturation'); this agrees with our observation that a main purpose for his making the sense-denotation distinction in the first place was the negative one of setting the notion of sense aside in order that it not obstruct or confuse the development of the theory at the level of denotation. We shall remain at this level, then, in this and the next two sections, and widen our purview again to include the 'realm of senses' as well as the 'realm of denotations' only in **7** when we come to the topic of assertion.

What then can be said of functions? We should recall here our differentiation at the beginning of **3** of simple and complex complete names, where a complex complete name was provisionally understood as a complete name containing a complete name as a proper part. By those lights, "9^2" and "3^2" and "the shirt of Nessus" were complex complete names. Since then, however, the category of complete names has been enlarged to include *sentences*; accordingly, "$3^2 = 9$", "3 is even" and "the shirt of Nessus caused the death of Hercules" will also be understood as complex complete names.

An incomplete name was provisionally understood as the result of removing one or more complete names from a complex complete name (as provisionally understood), a procedure that left gaps which we marked by open parentheses. In place of these gaps let us now use Frege's lower-case Greek consonants "ξ" and "ζ", thus writing instead of "$(\ )^2$" and "the shirt of $(\ )$", "ξ^2" and "the shirt of ξ". These letters will serve purely as gap-holders in incomplete names and have no other purpose; the point of using them will emerge when we widen our still restricted notion of incomplete name, for then we shall encounter various types of gaps.

Now a complex complete name of the kind we are considering is formed by completing an incomplete name by one or more complete names, depending upon the number of gaps; let us for now confine ourselves to one. Thus, completing "ξ^2" by "3" we obtain "3^2", completing "the shirt of ξ" by "Nessus" we obtain "the shirt of Nessus", completing "ξ is even" by "3" we obtain "3 is even", and so on. And Frege describes the *function* denoted by an incomplete name in an analogous way: we are to think of the completion of the i n c o m p l e t e name, resulting in a complete name, as the syntactical analogue of a 'saturation' *of the function,* as if the *function* had a gap; a function is an entity such that, saturated by an object, an argument, it results in an object, the value of the function for the former object as argument. So, just as "3^2" is the result of completing "ξ^2" with "3", likewise 3^2 (that is, 9) is the result of saturating ξ^2 with 3; 9 is 'what the function becomes on completion' *(das, wozu sie [= die Function] ergänzt wird*; cf. below, p. 34). Again, just as "3 is even" is the result of completing "ξ is even" with "3", likewise 3 is even (that is, the False) is the result of saturating ξ is even with 3.

All of this is of course entirely metaphorical and quite obscure. But Frege claims that only metaphor is possible, no further explanation can be given; for we have reached what is logically simple, a level of logical analysis so profound that he can convey his meaning only by 'hints'; he must rely upon the reader to 'meet him halfway' and 'not begrudge a pinch of salt'. This claim is perhaps unfortunate, for it suggests that Fregean functions are weird and exotic entities about which nothing clear or even intelligible can be said. (A large and unilluminating secondary literature has grown up about them that would appear to bear this out.) In order to see the matter more clearly let us first drop the use of the term "entity" in connection with functions (as in "unsaturated entity"); for it seems only to cause confusion. Now at one point Frege gives a perfectly clear specification of the circumstances under which an incomplete name of the kind before us is to be regarded as having a denotation: namely,

> A name of a first-level function of one argument has a *denotation* (*denotes* something, succeeds in *denoting*) if the proper name that results from this function-name by its argument-places' being filled by a proper name always has a denotation if the name substituted denotes something.[26]

The failure of this condition with respect to a given incomplete name "$\Phi(\xi)$"[27], then, is to be taken as analogous to (e.g.) the

[26]Cf. below, p. 84, also p. 88.

[27]Capital Greek letters are used here and in Frege's informal elucidations and illustrations 'as if they were names denoting something, without specifying what the denotation is'; cf. below, p. 38, n. 15. Thus

nonexistence of Nessus with respect to the complete name "Nessus"; in each case the situation is described in terms of denotationlessness of the name. In these terms, the question whether "ξ^2", for example, has denotation, should be viewed not as asking whether there exists an unsaturated entity ξ^2 that "ξ^2" names, but rather as asking whether every completion of "ξ^2" by a denoting complete name of the language is a denoting complete name of the language. (In fact, a further condition is also assumed: that the complete names resulting from completing the incomplete name by names denoting the same object, are names denoting the same object; we shall return to this in **6**.)

The controversial point is not whether Frege wished to apply the idea of *denotation* in the case of incomplete names in a sense as close as possible to that in which it was applied to complete names; as was observed in **3**, it is clear that he did. Nor need there be confusion as to what in concrete cases the ascription of denotation to an incomplete name was supposed to assert; that has just been cited. Rather, the ideas that do stand in need of justification are two. The first is the idea that an incomplete name *cannot* denote an *object*, so that the simple picture of denoting first evoked when we imagined the relation between (say) a proper name in the ordinary sense and the object (person, place, or thing) that it names—however generalized, attenuated and made abstract, as it has been by its progressive extensions, ending with its extension to cover sentences—*cannot* be meaningfully applied in the case of incomplete names. The second is the idea that nevertheless the condition

always results in a denoting complete name
upon completion by a denoting complete name

for incomplete names, sufficiently resembles the condition

denotes an object

for complete names, to warrant the use of language like "has denotation", "denotes something", "succeeds in denoting" and the like for incomplete names that satisfy it. These two

their status is roughly that of variables of the metalanguage ranging over the objects and functions in the universe of the object-language. They do not occur in asserted propositions of the system itself.

ideas together are what make up the doctrine that incomplete names have denotation, but denotation that is unsaturated. Frege never succeeded in giving a clear vindication of either of them. His attempts to justify the claim that incomplete names cannot denote objects all resort to metaphor, the metaphors all break down as unsupported metaphors must, and we are left with the plea that one can only 'hint'. And the attempts to justify the other claim, that incomplete names must nonetheless have denotation, consist entirely of assertions that the contrary is unthinkable.

Although I believe that a justification for both claims in a generally Fregean spirit can be given, it would take us sufficiently beyond what is actually to be found in his writings to render it an intrusion in an editorial Introduction, and so it seems best to defer it for another occasion[28]. Let us therefore proceed on the assumption that just as, if a complete name A satisfies the second condition mentioned above, we are entitled to express this fact in the form

"there exists an object that A denotes,"

so also, if an incomplete name B satisfies the first condition mentioned above, we are entitled to express this fact in the form

"there exists a function that B denotes."

It is indisputable that this assumption is held by Frege, whatever we may think of his attempts to substantiate it. And let us also assume, as he does, that if the first condition for the having of denotation is appropriate to a name—if the name is an incomplete name—then the second condition is *not* appropriate to it, and conversely, that if the second condition for the having of denotation is appropriate to a name—if it is a complete name—then the first condition is *not* appropriate to it. This assumption is made by Frege in the form: an incomplete name cannot denote an object but only a function, and a complete name cannot denote a function but only an object; but our formulation is preferable in that it expresses the distinction in terms of *two manners in which names may have denotation, rather than two types of 'entity' that names may denote.* The latter idiom is responsible for much of the obscurity surrounding the denotational

---

[28] It is discussed in my forthcoming paper, "Two Types of Denotation".

semantics of incomplete names.[29]

On these assumptions, then, we shall talk of functions as denoted by incomplete names, the circumstances under which an incomplete name denotes a function being as specified above. We shall also use Frege's terms "argument" and "value" for the denotations of the completing complete name and the resulting complex complete name respectively. The specification requires that an incomplete name be defined, or explained, for every object whatever as argument[30]; thus this requirement is not, as is sometimes thought, to be viewed primarily as a requirement of 'scientific precision', but stems from the manner of denoting appropriate to such names.

The incomplete names that we have so far considered are those that Frege calls *names of first-level functions*: functions whose arguments are objects (or arguments of type 1). Not only must such names (to denote) result in a denoting complete name upon completion by any denoting complete name; but moreover, the *only* names by which they are appropriately completed are complete names; the result of completing an incomplete name of this sort with an incomplete name is *not* a complete name. Thus names of first-level functions are defined over all objects, and also over objects only.

A first-level function whose value for every object as argument is a truth-value is a *first-level concept*; an incomplete name denoting a concept is a *concept-word*. Typically, since sentences are regarded as complete names, a concept-word

---

[29] It is partially responsible for the apparent paradox, "the concept *horse* is not a concept", which Frege notoriously attempted to shrug off in "Über Begriff und Gegenstand." A related symptom of the same difficulty occurs below, p. 37, note 12. It should be stressed here that our eschewal of the word "entity" is meant to attenuate a source of *philosophical* confusion, consisting in a certain picture of what anything called "denotation" has to be; it need not prevent us from dealing with higher-order quantification. This is explained further in the paper cited in note 28.

[30] In the form cited above, the requirement is weaker than this: that the incomplete name be defined for every object a complete name of which is formable in the language. It can be argued that this restriction is not in fact so confining as it may look; alternatively, one could extend the specification to include completion by variables as well as names.

would be the incomplete name resulting from removal of a complete name from a sentence. For first-level concepts the requirement that they be defined or explained for every object whatever as argument is thus the requirement that for any completion by a denoting complete name, the result be a complete name denoting either the True or the False. This is also described as the requirement that the Law of Excluded Middle hold for them, or, less happily, that concepts must 'have sharp boundaries'. [31]

We have confined ourselves to incomplete names that result in complete names upon completion by a single complete name: incomplete names denoting a function of one argument. Incomplete names denoting functions of two or more arguments are treated along the same lines; in practice Frege has no need for functions of more than two arguments (which is why only two gap-holders, "ξ" and "ζ", are required for incomplete names denoting first-level functions). A first-level function of two arguments whose value is invariably a truth-value is a *first-level relation*; an incomplete name denoting a relation is a *relation-word*.

We can approach the differentiation of functions according to *level* by widening our notion of a complex complete name: allowing a complex complete name to be a complete name having a name (but not necessarily a complete name) as a proper part. Certain incomplete names, i.e., first-level-function-names[32], form complex complete names only upon completion with complete names; the next class of incomplete names consists of those that form complex complete names only upon completion with first-level-function-names, and incomplete names in this class denote *second-level functions*. An incomplete name of this kind has a denotation if the result of completing it with a denoting first-level-function-name is invariably a denoting complete name. If this result is invariably a name of a truth-value then the incomplete name denotes a *second-level concept*. As in the first-level-function-name

$$\text{``}\Phi(\xi)\text{''} \text{ [33]},$$

---

[31]Less happily because the phrase again carries connotations of 'scientific precision' (versus, say, vagueness), which is not the point.

[32]The terminology is not Frege's, but naturally suggests itself.

[33]On the use of Greek capitals, cf. note 27 above.

the letter "ξ" is a gap-holder for a complete name, so in the second-level-function-name

$$\text{``}\Omega_{\beta}(\phi(\beta))\text{''},$$

the letter "ϕ" is a gap-holder for a first-level-function-name; "ψ" is also so used. The second "β" is a portion of the second-level-function-name placed so as to be ringed by the gap in any first-level-function-name occurring as name of an argument; it is keyed to the earlier subscript "β" in a manner suggested by the relation of an occurrence in the context following a variable-binding operator of a variable bound by that operator, to the occurrence of that variable in the operator itself.[34]

The most conspicuous incomplete names of this sort are the quantifiers: the universal quantifier denotes a certain second-level concept, whose value is the True if the argument is a first-level function having the True as value for every argument (i.e., if the argument is a first-level concept under which every object falls); for a first-level function as argument that does not satisfy this condition, the value of the second-level concept is the False.

Here a few fine points may be mentioned. The name "$\overset{a}{\smile}\Phi(a)$" denotes the value of this second-level concept, named

$$\text{``}\overset{a}{\smile}\phi(a)\text{''},$$

for the argument $\Phi(\xi)$; here the Gothic letter "a" discharges the office of a bound variable, but in Frege's schematism it is a syncategorematic piece of the function-name "$\overset{a}{\smile}\phi(a)$" and has no meaning of any kind whatever in isolation. (Frege once [35] ascribes to such letters the type of meaning that belongs to *free* variables (Roman letters) in his system, but this is a slip.) Thus variables are not 'bound' by quantifiers; instead of this they disappear entirely and are supplanted by inseverable parts of a certain second-level-concept-word. (For this reason Peano's term "apparent variable" is perhaps better suited to describe the Gothic letters than Hilbert's "bound variable".) Again,

---

[34]In fact, second-level-function-names are the exact analogues of (first-order) variable-binding operators, save for being *names* and not syncategorematic expressions; cf. 2 above. They are replaceable by free variables ('marks'); the Roman letter "*M*" is used for this purpose.

[35]Cf. p. 66 below.

there is no 'vacuous' quantification "for all x, $\mathbf{P}$", "x" not free in $\mathbf{P}$; for a second-level function cannot take an object (for instance, a truth-value) as argument. On the other hand, such curiosities are possible as "for all x, x"; this is the value of the second-level concept in question for the first-level function ξ, the first-level function whose value for every object as argument is that object itself[36]; since the value of the latter function is not the True for every argument, it follows that "for all x, x" denotes the False. (Therefore "it is not the case that for all x, x" denotes the True.) It might also be mentioned that this approach to quantification facilitates a perspicuous explanation of the so-called 'confinement laws', such as the equivalence of "$(x)(F(x) \to \mathbf{P})$" and "$(\exists x)F(x) \to \mathbf{P}$"[37].

Second-level functions $\Omega_{\beta}(\phi(\beta))$ whose arguments are first-level functions of one argument are said to take *arguments of type 2*; second-level functions

$$\Omega_{\beta,\gamma}(\phi(\beta,\gamma))$$

whose arguments $\Phi(\xi,\zeta)$ are first-level functions of two arguments are said to take *arguments of type 3*. As monadic quantification enters with the former, so multiple quantification enters with the latter, since among 'arguments of type 3' are first-level relations.

The interpretation of theorems of the first-order predicate calculus is then this: each such theorem asserts of every first-level function (of one or more arguments, as the case may be) that it satisfies a certain second-level condition; in Fregean idiom, it asserts that every first-level function 'falls within' a certain second-level concept, named by a more or less complex second-level-concept-word. Thus such a theorem as

$$\text{``} \vdash \left(\overset{a}{\underset{F(a)}{\rightharpoondown}} \mathbf{P} = \underset{a}{\overset{}{\rightharpoondown}} \mathbf{P} \right) \text{''} ,$$

as we might write it,

$$\text{``}(x)(F(x) \to \mathbf{P}) \leftrightarrow ((\exists x)F(x) \to \mathbf{P})\text{''} ,$$

asserts of every first-level function of one argument $F(\xi)$ that it

---

[36] Cf. p. 81 below. This does require us to delete the word "proper" from our prior characterization of an incomplete name.

[37] $\overset{a}{\rightharpoondown}\underset{F(a)}{\mathbf{P}} = \overset{a}{\rightharpoondown}\underset{\mathbf{P}}{F(a)} = \overset{a}{\rightharpoondown}\underset{\mathbf{P}}{F(a)} = \overset{}{\rightharpoondown}\underset{a\,F(a)}{\mathbf{P}}.$ Cf. below, p. 67.

falls within the second-level concept

$$\text{---}^{a}_{\phi(a)} P \;=\; \text{---}^{a}_{\phi(a)} P \;;$$

again, such a theorem as

$$\text{``} \text{---}^{e\ a}_{F(a,e)} \text{''}$$
$$\text{---}^{a\ e}_{F(a,e)}\ ,$$

as we might write it,

$$\text{``}(\exists x)(y)F(x,y) \rightarrow (y)(\exists x)F(x,y)\text{''}\,,$$

asserts of every first-level function of two arguments $F(\xi,\zeta)$ that it falls within the second-level concept

$$\text{---}^{e\ a}_{\phi(a,e)}$$
$$\text{---}^{a\ e}_{\phi(a,e)}\ .$$

Aside from the quantifiers the only other names of second-level functions that figure in the book are the names "$\acute{\epsilon}\,\phi(\epsilon)$" and "$\acute{a}\acute{\epsilon}\,\phi(\epsilon,a)$", of which the former is supposed to denote that second-level function whose value for each first-level function (of one argument) as argument is the course-of-values of that first-level function, and the latter is supposed to denote the analogous second-level function taking first-level functions of two arguments as argument. Thus these names would be *abstraction operators*[38] which, prefixed to a function-name, would give us a name of the course-of-values of the function: in particular, prefixed to a concept-word or predicate, would give us a name of the extension of the concept, or equivalently, of the class of objects of which the predicate was true. This interpretation breaks down due to inconsistency; in any case further discussion of it is better postponed for our consideration of courses-of-values in **6.**

The last type of incomplete name introduced comprises names of *third-level functions*: in particular, two names of *third-level concepts*, concepts taking second-level concepts as argument. Here the name "$\text{---}_{\beta}\Omega_{\beta}f(\beta)$" denotes the value of a certain third-level concept, named

$$\text{``}\text{---}_{\beta}\mu_{\beta}f(\beta)\text{''}\,,$$

for the argument $\Omega_{\beta}(\phi(\beta))$. (In the incomplete name mentioned above, the letter "μ" is a gap-holder for a second-level-function-name, parallel to "ϕ" for first-level-function-names and

---

[38] But cf. note 34 above.

"ξ" for complete names.) An example would be that in which the second-level function $\Omega_\beta(\phi(\beta))$ is the particular second-level concept $\smile^a\!\!\!-\phi(a)$, just encountered; the name in question would then be the name

$$\text{``}\underbrace{}\!-^a\!\!\mathfrak{f}(a)\text{''}.$$

This third-level concept has as value the True if the argument is a second-level function having the True as value for every first-level function (of one argument of type 2) as argument (i.e., if the argument is a second-level concept within which every such first-level function falls); for a second-level function that does not satisfy this condition, the value of the third-level concept is the False. Hence the name displayed above denotes the False; for not every first-level concept falls within $\smile^a\!\!\!-\phi(a)$— that is, not every concept is such that every object falls under it. Therefore

$$\text{``}\underbrace{}_{\frown}\!-^a\!\!\mathfrak{f}(a)\text{''}$$

denotes the True. On the other hand, the two second-level concepts mentioned two paragraphs back *are* well-known instances of second-level concepts within which every first-level function of the appropriate number of arguments falls. For this reason

$$\text{``}\underbrace{}\!\!\left(\overset{a}{\underset{\mathfrak{f}(a)}{\boxed{}}}\mathrm{P} = \underset{a}{\underset{\frown\ \mathfrak{f}(a)}{\boxed{}}}\mathrm{P}\right)\text{''}$$

denotes the True; and so does

$$\text{``}\underbrace{}\!\!\underset{\frown}{^e}\!\!\overset{a}{\frown}\!\mathfrak{f}(a,e)\text{''}$$
$$\underset{a}{\boxed{}}\underset{\frown}{^e}\!\mathfrak{f}(a,e)\ ,$$

which is formed by use of the other third-level-concept-word, "$\underbrace{}\!\mu_{\beta,\gamma}\mathfrak{f}(\beta,\gamma)$", standing to second-level functions taking arguments of type 3 just as "$\underbrace{}\!\mu_\beta\mathfrak{f}(\beta)$" stands to second-level functions taking arguments of type 2.

The Gothic letter "$\mathfrak{f}$" in these concept-words discharges the office of what would nowadays be called a bound function-variable; but as with the "a" in quantification over objects, the "$\mathfrak{f}$" is regarded as an inseverable piece of the concept-word and has no meaning of any kind in isolation.

5

Name and mark. We have surveyed the 'realm of denotations' from the standpoint of *names* denoting these denotations: simple and complex names of objects, first-level functions and concepts, second-level functions and concepts, and so on, taking note also of some further differentiations (for example, between second-level functions taking arguments of type 2 and those taking arguments of type 3). Over and above the names are the *Roman marks*, or, as we should call them, *free variables*. Unlike the Gothic letters, the Roman letters do have meaning of a certain kind in isolation: but their role is not to *denote*, as names do, but rather to *indicate indefinitely* or ambiguously (*unbestimmt andeuten*). What this means is expressed in more recent terminology by saying that to a Roman letter is assigned a range: for a Roman *object-mark* or *mark of an object*, the range is the totality of objects; for a Roman *mark of a first-level function of one argument* the range is the totality of first-level functions of one argument, and so on. The objects, or functions, in the range of a Roman mark are what now would be called *values*[39] of this Roman mark. Marks, like names, may be simple or complex; the characteristic case is that in which a complex mark is composed of, say, a simple mark and a function-name; since Frege uses the Roman lower-case letters "*a*", "*b*", "*c*", ..., for simple object-marks, an example would be the complex mark composed of the simple object-mark "*a*" and the function-name "$\xi + 3$". The complex object-mark "$a + 3$" would have as values[39] (Frege says, would indicate indefinitely) the values of the function $\xi + 3$ for the values[39] of the simple object-mark "*a*".

Perhaps it is difficult for us to appreciate the liberation that this conception made possible. For it was customary in Frege's day to understand variables as if they *denoted* or named a *variable entity* ('variable magnitude', 'variable quantity', or what not), of which no intelligible account could then be given. In some quarters such an idea has inexplicitly prevailed even more recently. Frege not only freed the notion of a variable from its restriction to 'magnitudes' or 'quantities', but what is much more important, laid down a clear conception according to which the semantical role of a variable was not that of *denoting* a

---

[39] Of course, this is not the same use of "value" as that in which a function is said to have a value for a certain argument; in this use it is an *expression* of a certain kind that is said to have objects or functions as values. But there seems to be no other term (though Frege's "indicate" could be bent to the purpose).

varying or indefinite entity, but that of *indicating* (having as values[39]) the members of a range of perfectly definite entities, the selfsame entities *denoted* by the names that could appropriately replace the variable.[40] Like many great advances, it seems quite simple now.

6

Function and course-of-values. Concept and extension. The issues involved in the distinction between function and course-of-values, concept and extension, are the most difficult in Frege's work, and also the most widely misunderstood. An additional, very large complication is that the theory of extensions is inconsistent. But before dealing with that matter, we must first settle the severe problems of interpretation surrounding the notions in their originally intended form.

The notion of a course-of-values is fairly easily related to more recent notions as approximately a function-in-extension[41]; thus expressions of the form

$$\text{``}\grave{\epsilon}(\dots\epsilon\dots)\text{''}$$

encountered in Frege could be read as meaning much the same as expressions in lambda-notation of the form

$$\text{``}\lambda x(\dots x\dots)\text{''},$$

or where the lambda-terminology is defined in terms of class-terminology, of the form

$$\text{``}\hat{y}\hat{x}(y = \dots x\dots)\text{''},$$

that is, as denoting the class of ordered couples $x;y$ such that y is the value of the function $\dots\xi\dots$ for the argument x. Thus the name

$$\text{``}\grave{\epsilon}(\epsilon+7)\text{''}$$

would denote a class containing such ordered couples as 0;7, 1;8, 2;9. It must be borne in mind, however, that for Frege the smooth-breathing abstraction operator that forms course-of-values-names is *primitive*, and is not defined in terms of class abstraction or in any other way. On the contrary, what corresponds

---

[40] Since there are function-marks as well as object-marks, we are here technically infringing the policy regarding "entity" adopted on p. xxvii; this should be regarded as an expository expedient and not as nullification of the policy. Cf. also note 29 above.

[41] Cf. **2** above.

in this theory to a *class* is a species of course-of-values: the course-of-values of a function whose value for every object as argument is a truth-value, such a course-of-values being called the extension of a concept. (If $\acute{\epsilon}(\cdots\epsilon\cdots)$ is the extension of a concept, then thought of in terms of classes it would be the class of ordered couples $x;y$ such that y is the truth-value of *x's falling under the concept* $\cdots\xi\cdots$; thus the name

$$\text{``}\acute{\epsilon}(\epsilon^2 = 4)\text{''},$$

denoting the extension of the concept *square root of four*, would denote a class containing such ordered couples as

$$2; \text{ the True}$$
$$0; \text{ the False}$$
$$-2; \text{ the True}$$
$$-4; \text{ the False.})$$

From this we see that the notions of a course-of-values and of an extension are reasonably familiar. The difficulties arise when we turn to Frege's conception of the relation between a course-of-values and the function whose course-of-values it is, and the relation between an extension and the concept whose extension it is.

One of the most widespread misconceptions of Frege's theory has been the view that the denotation of a function-name (of what we have called an incomplete name) is a course-of-values; that for the special case of concept-words, the denotation is the extension of a concept. Allied with this is the view that where Frege speaks of a *function*, or a *concept*, he intends something standing to the function-name or concept-word not as its *denotation* but as its *sense*[42]. Now this certainly is a misconception: Frege repeatedly insists that (1) the denotation of a function-name is a function, that of a concept-word is a concept, and that (2) a function is fundamentally different from a course-of-values because the latter is an *object*; likewise the extension of a concept is an *object*, and objects are totally unlike functions in being 'saturated'. This means that the distinction between

---

[42]This interpretation is assumed in Carnap's *Meaning and Necessity* (Chicago, 1947), pp. 125-127, 130; cf. also Mates, *Stoic Logic* (Berkeley and Los Angeles, 1953), pp. 20, 24-25; also Wells, "Frege's Ontology," *Review of Metaphysics*, 4 (1950-1951), 537-573; also Quine, "On Frege's Way Out," *Mind*, 64 (1955), 145-159.

function and course-of-values, concept and extension, is meant to be made within the system *at the level of denotation*; a function $\Phi(\xi)$ is not the sense expressed by a function-name, nor is it the sense of anything; it is the denotation of a function-name. And a course-of-values $\acute{\epsilon}\Phi(\epsilon)$ is denoted, not by a function-name, but by a course-of-values-name.

If a course-of-values $\acute{\epsilon}\Phi(\epsilon)$ does not stand to the corresponding first-level function $\Phi(\xi)$ as denotation to sense, then how *are* they related? A course-of-values is an object that is determined, for the function, by what value the function has for every object as argument; thus two functions whose values for every argument are the same are said to determine the same course-of-values, and it is taken also that any two functions that determine the same course-of-values must have the same values for every argument. Likewise the extension $\acute{\epsilon}\Psi(\epsilon)$ of the concept $\Psi(\xi)$ is determined by the truth-value, for every object x, of x's *falling under the concept* $\Psi(\xi)$; if for two concepts precisely the same objects fall under each, then they are said to have the same extension, and (as before) conversely.

It is clear from the foregoing that courses-of-values and extensions are meant to be *extensional*, in the classical sense in which sets, for example, are in other theories said to be extensional because they are identical when their members are identical. It must be clearly understood that in Frege's theory *functions and concepts are also extensional; they are not distinguished from courses-of-values and the extensions of concepts on this ground, but on the ground that courses-of-values and the extensions of concepts are objects whereas functions and concepts are not.* The point is stressed because of the wide circulation of the contrary idea, which runs thus: that the circumstance of two functions' having the same value for every argument, while sufficient to preclude any difference between their courses-of-values, is not sufficient to preclude difference between the functions themselves; in the case of concepts, that the concepts $\Psi(\xi)$ and $X(\xi)$ might differ although precisely the same objects fell under each, and the extensions $\acute{\epsilon}\Psi(\epsilon)$ and $\acute{\epsilon}X(\epsilon)$ were accordingly the same. This is to regard functions and concepts as subject to some stricter or narrower criterion of individuation than that for courses-of-values and extensions, and it is this idea that in turn makes it plausible to think of function standing to course-of-values as sense to denotation.

Now the notion that functions and concepts are nonextensional does find apparent confirmation in certain passages in Frege; if the notion is incorrect these passages must be otherwise explained. One type of remark runs as follows: from the fact that

$$\text{``}\underset{a}{\smile} \Phi(a) = \Psi(a)\text{''}$$

denotes the True, we may infer that $\text{``}\acute{\epsilon}\Phi(\epsilon)\text{''}$ denotes the same as $\text{``}\acute{\epsilon}\Psi(\epsilon)\text{''}$; but we may not infer that

$$\Phi(\xi) = \Psi(\xi).$$

This creates the impression that the functions may yet differ where the courses-of-values coincide. Thus, we may not write

$$\text{``}(\xi^2 - 1) = (\xi + 1)(\xi - 1)\text{''}$$

or, apparently,

$$\text{``}(\xi^2 - 4\xi) = \xi(\xi - 4)\text{''}[43]$$

And one is tempted to conclude that functions are nonextensional. Another type of passage is illustrated by the remark in *Grundlagen* that 'concepts can have the same extension without coinciding [*zusammenfallen*][44]'. And again, there is the following:

> One may perhaps get the impression from these explanations that in the conflict between extensional and intensional logicians [*Logiker des Umfangs und [die] des Inhalts*] I am taking the side of the latter. In fact I do hold that the concept is logically prior to its extension, and I regard as futile the attempt to base the extension of a concept as a class not on the concept but on individual things.[45]

In the last, the statement that "the concept is logically prior to its extension" has to do with distinguishing an extension from a collection or aggregate or sum in the sense of a whole made up of parts; Frege held that in grasping the notion of an extension one is inevitably, whether explicitly or tacitly, appealing to the notion of a concept. What is relevant here is that once again the relation of extension to concept is apparently being

---

[43] For the first case, cf. *Grundgesetze*, Vol. II, p. 148; for the second, cf. *Function und Begriff*, p. 9.

[44] *Grundlagen*, p. 80.

[45] "Kritische Beleuchtung einiger Punkte in E. Schröders *Vorlesungen über die Algebra der Logik*," p. 455.

construed on the model of extensional to intensional.

To see that this appearance is misleading, let us recall the principle stated in **4** above specifying the circumstances under which a function-name has a denotation: namely, if every completion of it by a denoting complete name is a denoting complete name. This is formal mode, concerned with the name's having denotation, for what would be expressed in material mode in terms of a function's determining a value for every object as argument: what it is, in the terms of **4**, for a function to exist. A further statement, for the case of concept-words, is this:

> A definition of a concept (of a possible predicate) must be complete; it must specify unambiguously for every object whether or not it falls under the concept (whether or not the predicate is truly assertible of it). Thus there must not be any object for which the definition leaves in doubt whether it falls under the concept—although for us men, with our defective knowledge, the question may not always be decidable. . . . Any object Δ that you choose to take either falls under the concept Φ or does not fall under it; *tertium non datur*. (*Grundgesetze*, Vol. II, p. 69).

Now, do these principles differentiate functions with any greater strictness than their courses-of-values? The answer is that in themselves they lay down no degree of differentiation whatever, but they are significant in confirming the general impression that the *whole* nature of a function consists in its determining a value (for concepts, a truth-value) for every object as argument, and that there is therefore no room for a differentiation among functions that would not be manifested in any difference in their values for any object as argument.

It will be helpful to contrast the situation here with that in *Principia Mathematica*. In *Principia* a distinction is made between so-called *propositional functions* on the one hand and *classes* on the other; in fact, the primitive notation of *Principia* is a notation for propositional functions, and that for classes is introduced into the theory by means of contextual definitions. A propositional function is apparently supposed to be a function whose values are (not truth-values but) *propositions*, entities somewhat like a Fregean *Gedanke*.[46] Now the class of objects

---

[46] Sometimes "propositional function" is used in *Principia* to mean an *expression*: an open sentence or predicate or concept-word, but this confusion is of no importance to us here.

that are f, $\hat{x}f(x)$, is composed of those objects for which as argument the value of the propositional function $f\hat{x}$ is a true proposition. If propositional functions $f\hat{x}$ and $g\hat{x}$ have as values true propositions for exactly the same objects, i.e., if

$$(x)(f(x) \leftrightarrow g(x)),$$

then the classes $\hat{x}f(x)$ and $\hat{x}g(x)$ are the same, i.e.,

$$\hat{x}f(x) = \hat{x}g(x);$$

but it does not follow that the propositional functions are themselves the same; for some or all objects a, $f(a)$ and $g(a)$ may be different *propositions*, though one will be a *true* proposition if and only if the other is. Thus propositional functions are much more finely discriminated among than classes, by way of a finer discrimination among their values than is afforded merely by the circumstance of truth or falsehood; [47] in this sense classes are extensional, but propositional functions are not.

For Frege, the finest discrimination among concepts will differentiate them no more strictly than their extensions; for their values are truth-values. And in general, if functions have everywhere the same value for the same argument, so that their courses-of-values are the same, no way is given of drawing any further logical distinctions between them. (Cf. also p. 95 below.)

Thus the sole difference between concept and extension, between function and course-of-values, is the difference of *saturation*: extension and course-of-values are *objects*; concept and function are not. In that case, how are we to explain Frege's puzzling remarks cited two pages back? Let us recall once again the conditions mentioned on p. xxviii in **4** under which incomplete and complete names respectively are thought of as denoting. In these terms, if two complete names A and B (including course-of-values-names) 'have the same denotation', the situation may be described thus,

> there exists an object that both A *and* B *denote*;

but what will and must correspond to this for the case of two *incomplete* names C and D will be,

---

[47] *How* much more finely is a question left unanswered in *Principia*. The description given here is of the first edition; in his Introduction to the second edition Russell modified the notion of 'propositional function' to make it practically the same thing as Frege's 'concept'.

> *the completions of* C *and* D *by complete names de-*
> *noting the same object* [= *argument*] *are always*
> *complete names denoting the same object* [= *value*];

and accordingly, as the former circumstance stands to the first-level relation

$$\xi = \zeta \, ,$$

the latter circumstance will stand to the second-level relation

$$\underset{a}{\smile} \phi(a) = \psi(a) \, .$$

Thus the explanation is to be found in the fact, noted (although not fully explored) in **4**, that there are irreducibly two manners in which names may have denotation: one appropriate to complete, the other to incomplete names. The reason why we cannot infer, for example, from truth of

$$``\acute{\epsilon}(\epsilon^2 - 1) = \acute{\epsilon}((\epsilon + 1)(\epsilon - 1))"$$

to something of the form

$$``(\xi^2 - 1) = (\xi + 1)(\xi - 1)"$$

is not that the second might be false where the first was true, as is possible with the corresponding cases in *Principia*, but that the second either makes no sense at all—employing as it does a condition appropriate for complete names having the same denotation where what is needed is the quite different second-level condition for incomplete names—or else denotes not a truth-value at all, but a first-level concept under which every object falls. (The same considerations would rule out even, e.g.,

$$``(\xi^2 - 1) = (\xi^2 - 1)"\,;$$

if the difficulty were the nonextensionality of functions, we should expect this test at least to be one that the most ultra-intensional of entities could pass.)

The reason why 'concepts can have the same extension without coinciding' is the same: the word "coincide" [*zusammen-fallen*] is used exclusively for the relation of identity appropriate to objects[48], a relation in which the denotations of concept-words—even of concept-words that 'have the same denotation' in

---

[48] "*Zusammenfallen*" characteristically occurs when Frege is explaining his use of "*Gleichheit*" to mean the same as "*Identität*", conceivable only for objects. Cf. "Über Sinn und Bedeutung," p. 25, note, Frege's Introduction below, p. 6, and the passage quoted in the next paragraph.

the manner appropriate to them—cannot stand.

All of this is confirmed by the following passage:

> For the mathematician, a definition of *conic section* as *line of intersection of a plane with the surface of a circular cone* is no more right and no more wrong than a definition of it as *plane curve with an equation of the second degree in Cartesian coördinates*. Which definition he chooses—one of these two, or some other again—depends entirely on reasons of suitability to his particular purposes, although these expressions neither have [= express] the same sense nor evoke the same ideas or images. I do not mean by this that a concept and the extension of a concept are one and the same; rather, coinciding in extension is a necessary and sufficient criterion for the holding between concepts of the relation corresponding to identity for objects. (Identity does not in fact, properly speaking, hold for concepts.) Let me remark here that I use the word "identical" [*gleich*], unless otherwise specified, in the sense of "not different", "coinciding" [*zusammenfallend*], "identical" [*identisch*].[49]

Thus far we have been considering the relation of concept and extension as Frege conceived it prior to 1902 and the news of the contradiction; now let us attend briefly to his reaction to that, as recorded in the epilogue to the second volume of *Grundgesetze* translated here as Appendix II. We observed in **2** above that the inconsistency proves to arise from the simultaneous maintaining of the two theses, (1) that to every first-level concept $\Phi(\xi)$ there answers a certain object $\acute{\epsilon}\Phi(\epsilon)$ answering to it as extension, whose identity-condition is that provided in Basic Law V, namely,

$$(\acute{\epsilon} f(\epsilon) = \acute{a} g(a)) = (\overset{a}{\smile} f(a) = g(a)),$$

and (2) that this object is a full-fledged or 'proper' object, meaning that it is an admissible argument for any first-level concept whatever.

In assessing the situation Frege was aware that setting it right meant revoking or modifying at least one of these. To revoke the second thesis would be to move toward a *theory of types* for extensions; Frege considers this idea but rejects it,

---

[49] Frege's review of Husserl's *Philosophie der Arithmetik*, p. 320; italics mine.

for reasons that he does not succeed in making wholly clear, although it is clear enough that it would entail a vast complication of his theory and invalidate most of the proofs as originally given. Thus we turn to the first thesis. This may be approached in various ways. One is, to confine its applicability to something less than '*every* first-level concept', thus ruling that not every concept *f* determines an extension, or (in different words) is subject to the principle of class *abstraction*

$$(\exists y)(x)(f(x) \leftrightarrow x \,\epsilon\, y),$$

although it may still be allowed that two concepts determine the same extension under the circumstances specified in Basic Law V if they determine extensions at all. The problem is then to supply a general characterization of the category of concepts regarded as susceptible to abstraction, the rest being immune, construing this category as liberally as practicable without inconsistency. This general attitude has been the genesis of *axiomatic set theory*, and alternative methods of specifying the category in question have led to the development of a very wide field under continually more intensive cultivation since Zermelo initiated the approach in 1908.

But Frege's approach to the first thesis is rather different, in an interesting way. It emerges from his discussion of the paradox, much more clearly (or at any rate more forcibly) than it has at any point before, that he has been thinking of Basic Law V as reflecting a situation of the following kind: there is a certain *second*-level function that assigns to each first-level concept (i.e., that has as value for each first-level concept as argument) an extension, and this second-level function assigns the same extension to two concepts if and only if precisely the same objects fall under each.[50] We thus have two conditions placed on this second-level function:

(Va) if the first-level concepts $\Phi(\xi)$ and $\Psi(\xi)$ are such that precisely the same objects fall under each, the second-level function assigns them the same extension.

This is no news to us; it merely follows from the extensionality

---

[50] Strictly, if precisely the same objects fall under each we should not refer to them as 'two', by the previous discussion; from this point of view, the half of Basic Law V given the name "Va" is simply a consequence of the denotation of the whole expression "$\acute{\epsilon}\Phi(\epsilon)$" being a function of the denotations of the parts "$\Phi(\xi)$" and "$\acute{\epsilon}\phi(\epsilon)$".

of concepts[51]. But furthermore:

(Vb) if the first-level concepts $\Phi(\xi)$ and $\Psi(\xi)$ are *not* such that precisely the same objects fall under each, then the second-level function must assign them different extensions.

Or, equivalently,

if the first-level concept $\Phi(\xi)$ is assigned the extension E, then for *every* first-level concept assigned this extension E, exactly the same objects must fall under it as fall under $\Phi(\xi)$.

It is this condition (Vb) that is paradoxical; in our present terms the argument runs thus. Consider the concept

[*object that*] *is the extension assigned some*
concept under which it does not fall.

Call this concept $\Omega(\xi)$. The second-level function assigns to this concept $\Omega(\xi)$ an extension. Furthermore, by Vb, for *every* first-level concept assigned this extension, precisely the same objects must fall under it as fall under $\Omega(\xi)$. Now we ask whether this extension falls under $\Omega(\xi)$ or does not fall under $\Omega(\xi)$; it must do one or the other if extensions are 'proper objects'. Suppose that it *does* fall under $\Omega(\xi)$. Then it is the extension assigned some concept under which it does not fall. But in that case, by Vb, it cannot fall under any concept to which it is assigned as extension, and therefore it does not fall under $\Omega(\xi)$. On the other hand, suppose that it *does not* fall under $\Omega(\xi)$. Then it is not the extension assigned to some concept under which it does not fall. But in that case, by Vb, it is not the extension assigned to any concept under which it does not fall, i.e., it must fall under every concept to which it is assigned as extension, therefore it falls under $\Omega(\xi)$.

Now, to conclude from this that certain concepts (such as $\Omega(\xi)$, for example) should be assigned *no* extension, as would be the case in a typical system of axiomatic set theory, would be in Frege's eyes to abandon the second-level function $\dot{\epsilon}\phi(\epsilon)$; for functions must be defined over every fitting argument—in this case we have an ostensible function of one argument of type 2, which if not defined over every first-level function of one argument is not a function at all. If we wish at all to have a theory of extensions, of classes, the function $\dot{\epsilon}\phi(\epsilon)$ must be retained, in its full range of applicability to arguments of type 2,

---

[51]Cf. note 50 above.

at all costs.

So instead Frege tries the tack of withdrawing the condition that two first-level concepts may be assigned the same extension only if precisely the same objects fall under each. This means revoking Vb, weakening it to some, thus far unspecified degree. Frege is painfully aware that the cost of doing so is the high one of having to abandon the claim that the function $\acute{\epsilon}\phi(\epsilon)$ gives as values extensions (or classes) in the received, or natural, or intuitive sense of the term, and his hope of finding some such function clearly dies very hard indeed. Not only that, but any tampering with Vb may restore consistency to the axioms of *Grundgesetze* only at the cost of invalidating all the proofs, save for that handful which do not depend upon it; and with them will disappear the hope of vindicating 'logicism', the theory that numbers are 'logical objects', and all the rest of it. But obviously there is no choice.

In fact, that Vb must be modified appears also from a more general argument, belatedly discovered by Frege in his efforts of the summer and autumn of 1902 to locate the precise cause of the difficulty: an argument showing that quite generally for *any* second-level function of one argument of type 2 there exist first-level concepts for which, as argument, the second-level function yields the same value V, but which are not such that precisely the same objects fall under each—namely, V falls under one and not under the other. If $\acute{\epsilon}\phi(\epsilon)$ is a function of this sort, as Frege had imagined, such pairs of concepts would be assigned the same extension although the condition $\overset{a}{\smile}\phi(a) = \psi(a)$ was not satisfied.

The question is then what weaker condition should be taken as necessary for coincidence of extension, what exceptions to the condition $\overset{a}{\smile}\phi(a) = \psi(a)$ are permissible. On the basis of his very hurried analysis of the problem, Frege snatched at the result just mentioned, applying it to this case so as to assert that where two concepts determine the same extension without standing in the relation $\overset{a}{\smile}\phi(a) = \psi(a)$, the object falling under the one and not under the other must invariably be their common extension and only this. Thus instead of

(Vb) $\acute{\epsilon}f(\epsilon) = \acute{a}g(a) \rightarrow (x)(f(x) \leftrightarrow g(x))$,

we make the condition this:

$\acute{\epsilon}f(\epsilon) = \acute{a}g(a) \rightarrow (x)(x \neq \acute{\epsilon}f(\epsilon) \ \& \ x \neq \acute{a}g(a) \rightarrow (f(x) \leftrightarrow g(x)))$.

And instead of what would correspond to

(1) $$f(y) \leftrightarrow y \in \hat{x}f(x),$$

we obtain:

(1') $$y \neq \hat{x}f(x) \rightarrow (y \in \hat{x}f(x) \leftrightarrow f(y)).$$

This modification of Vb is enough to block the reasoning leading to the original Russell paradox. Frege hoped that by it consistency had been restored, but this has proved to be not the case; the discrepancy from the naive ideal allowed by the emendation of Vb is not enough to prevent new contradictions from arising[52]. Also, as Frege feared, many of the proofs do break down in the revised system and to all appearances cannot easily be set right; a conspicuous example is the proof in the first volume of *Grundgesetze* that there exist infinitely many cardinal numbers[53].

Frege's specific method of dealing with extensions broke down because of the paradoxes. On the other hand, this should not be regarded as discrediting the basic idea behind this method, which is that of developing a theory of extensions, or classes, within a higher-order logic (in his terms, within a theory of higher-level functions and concepts); such an idea does not seem intrinsically incapable of being combined with safeguards against the paradoxes so as to produce theories both workable and interesting.

7

Name (or mark) of a truth-value and assertion. So far we have discussed two types of expressions: *names*, which are said to *denote*, and *marks*, which are said to *indicate*. Expressions of both these types may be complete or incomplete, simple or complex; but the basic differentiation of semantical role, paralleled by distinctness of types of expression, is supposed to be that between denoting and indicating. Now we must consider a third semantical role, thus far left out of account: that of *asserting* as true; this is played by a third category of expression known as *assertions*.

In order to make the desired c o m p a r i s o n s, let us adopt a

---

[52] Cf. Sobociński, "L'Analyse de l'antinomie russellienne par Lesniewski," *Methodos*, 1 (1949), 220-228; Quine, *op. cit.*; Geach, "On Frege's Way Out," *Mind*, 65 (1956), 408-409.

[53] *Grundgesetze*, Vol. I, pp. 137-144.

manner of speaking suggested[54], although not conformed to, by Frege: saying that by the use of a name that denotes a certain object, a person *designates* that object. Thus "designates" would differ from "denotes" in referring, not to a semantical property of an expression—the property, for example, that belongs to a complete name A if there exists an object x such that A denotes x—but rather to a certain use made by a person of an expression with respect to the denotation of that expression. "The Parthenon" denotes the Parthenon; but by use of "the Parthenon" I designate the Parthenon. Now we have been employing the word "sentence" to mean a name of a certain sort, namely one that expresses a sense, a thought (*Gedanke*), and denotes a denotation, a truth-value. We have also decided to call the relation borne by the sense expressed by a name to the denotation denoted by the name, *being a sense of.*[55] That a certain thought is a sense of a certain truth-value is an objective fact that obtains independent of human knowledge; a sentence merely expresses this thought and denotes this truth-value, both of which are antecedently 'there'. By the use of a sentence, as hitherto understood, I merely designate the truth-value—for example, the True—of which the thought expressed by the sentence is a sense; but I do not thereby assert, and I may not even know, which truth-value this is. A quite different activity is my use of a sentence to assert that the denotation of which the thought it expresses is a sense *is* the True. This activity is what Frege calls *judging* that something is the case (*urtheilen, dass etwas der Fall sei*).

The foregoing is not a definition of "judgment", and Frege holds that a definition is not possible; judgment is *sui generis* (*etwas ganz Eigenartiges und Unvergleichliches*); it is figuratively described as 'the advance from the thought to the truth-value', as 'not the mere comprehension of a thought, but the acknowledgement of its truth'[56]. In the late essay "Die Verneinung" occurs the suggestion, 'we are probably best in accord with ordinary usage if we take a judgment to be an *act* of judging, as a leap is an act of leaping. ... Judging, we may say, is

[54] Cf. below, p. 35. (But Frege generally uses "*bezeichnen*" interchangeably with "*bedeuten*".)

[55] Cf. 3 above.

[56] "Uber Sinn und Bedeutung," pp. 34-35. Cf. below, pp. 37-38.

acknowledging the truth of a thought. . . . If a judgment is an act, it happens at a certain time and thereafter belongs to the past. With an act there also belongs an agent, and we do not know the act completely if we do not know the agent.'[57] Thus judgment is like designation, and unlike denoting, in being irreducibly the act of a mind.

Of course the activity of judging, like that of designating, is not confined to instances of the explicit utilization of a name—for instance, by writing it down or uttering it aloud—these are merely conspicuous particular cases of activities that can be, or could be imagined, carried on without the appearance of any linguistic expression as intermediary vehicle. On the other hand, relative to linguistic expressions, the policy of paralleling distinct semantical roles by distinct types of expression dictates that a type of expression should be introduced that stands to *judging* as the category of names stands to *designating*. Thus we are led to the category of *assertions*; an assertion is an expression formed from a name of a truth-value by prefixing the assertion-sign or judgment-stroke "$\vdash$"; this sign is not a name, and not a mark, but a sign of a wholly special kind[58]. Also, a sign beginning with the judgment-stroke is not a name or a mark. 'For example, with "$\vdash 2 + 3 = 5$" we assert: $2 + 3$ is identical with 5. Thus here we are not merely inscribing a [name of] a truth-value, as in "$2 + 3 = 5$", but also at the same time saying that this truth-value is the True. (The judgment-stroke cannot be used to form a functional expression, because it does not serve in combination with other signs to designate an object. "$\vdash 2 + 3 = 5$" designates nothing; it asserts something.)'[59]

Not only is the sign "$\vdash$" not a name or mark, nor a constituent of any name or mark; equally it is not a sign of the metalanguage appearing in the office of "it is provable (or, a theorem) that": it is, rather (like the complex signs prefixed by it), an integral part of the object-language itself. It differs from all other signs in the kind of meaning belonging to it; by a *name*, an object (or function) is simply singled out by way of a certain sense, i.e., as that object (or function) of which the sense expressed by the

---

[57] "Die Verneinung", p. 151n.

[58] Cf. below, p. 82.

[59] *Function und Begriff*, p. 22. Here "designates" means the same as "denotes".

name is a sense; but by an *assertion*, the sense expressed by the name to which the judgment-stroke is prefixed is asserted to be a sense of the True. (This is not a repetition of the contrast made three paragraphs back; there we were concerned with designation versus judgment, two activities; here we are differentiating two types of expression with respect to kind of meaning or semantical role. Also, it is no more a *definition* of "assertion" than the former was a definition of "judgment".)

An assertion may also be constructed out of the judgment-stroke and a Roman mark of a truth-value; this case reduces to one in which the Roman mark is replaced by a name expressing a universal quantification[60].

The rules of inference are formulated not for names or marks of truth-values but for assertions, although their informal justifications are carried out in terms of the corresponding names and marks.

This part of the theory, distinguishing assertions from other expressions, has certain great attractions; but it is also puzzling. It has the wider advantages, not essentially connected with construing sentences as names, that go in general with distinguishing between the assertive and nonassertive use of a sentence; e.g., for dealing with the occurrence of sentences in sentential compounds, such as negative sentences and conditionals. If sentences express propositions or 'thoughts', as they may be regarded as doing without being regarded as names, then the propositional compound (called by Frege the *Gedankengefüge*) expressed by a sentential compound cannot be properly explained if each individual sentence occurring in the sentential compound is interpreted as *asserting* that the thought which it expresses is *true*. These and related matters were very thoroughly discussed by Frege in his last published essays, in which, however, the notions of denotation and of name had receded remarkably into the background[61]. In the narrower sense directly relevant to *Grundgesetze*, the distinction is what makes it possible to press the analogy between sentences and names, the advantages of which have already been discussed. Otherwise we should find ourselves repeatedly blocked by the fact

---

[60]Cf. above, 5, and below, p. 90.

[61]The essays are "Der Gedanke," "Die Verneinung," and "Gedankengefüge."

that precisely what differentiates sentences from other expressions is the fact that they can be used to assert something, a use in which the analogy with names is much less persuasive.

But there is a puzzling aspect relating to the status of false assertions, in the sense of thoughts assertively declared to be thoughts of the True that are in fact not so. If judging is an act, then, like other acts, it can be performed well or badly; in our attempts to designate the True our aim is sometimes inaccurate where yet we claim (wrongly yet in good faith) that we have succeeded. Of course, this much is obvious; and Frege never claims that assertion is infallible. The difficulty is rather that the notions of truth and falsehood seem to be turning up twice over in the theory, once within the domain of individuals in the guise of the 'logical objects' the True and the False, and then again at a different level as success versus failure, commendable versus exceptionable execution, of the act of asserting: and whatever may be said of either of these separately, it certainly is not clear offhand how they bear upon each other, nor whether separately or together they constitute a satisfactory explication of the notions of truth and falsehood that we are ordinarily accustomed to employ.[62]

A second, related point is this. The Fregean notion of judgment singles out one particular species of names, i.e., names denoting the True, and introduces relative to them a certain activity, that of judging or asserting; now it may be wondered why it is that the True, among all objects, is accorded this special treatment—why, for example, it would not be equally reasonable to introduce a sign to be prefixed to expressions denoting the number 9, signalizing the agent's 'advance from the sense to the denotation' of *such* expressions, his positing that the sense expressed by the expression *is* a sense of the number 9. The obvious retort is that the theory simply presupposes our interest in truth, and since in the theory true sentences, like all sentences, are names, the theory is simply reflecting this prior interest of ours by introducing an activity of 'advance from sense to denotation' relative to these names rather than others; but that the theory should not be expected to furnish us with an

---

[62] A similar point is made by Dummett in "Truth," *Proceedings of the Aristotelian Society* (1958-1959), 141-162, to which I owe the phrasing of the last clause.

explanation of this prior interest. This response has some merit: one should not ask that the theory explain our addiction to what within it assumes the guise of designating the True; but the difficulty is that it is not clear how any explanation whatever could be given that from the standpoint of the theory would not appear completely *ad hoc*; once (if ever) we are thoroughly persuaded of the propriety of taking the True to be one object among others (and certain sentences to be its names), then to the degree of our persuasion the sudden preëminence into which it is thrust by the advent of assertion will be to that degree difficult for us to understand, given what has gone before. There is nothing wrong with holding that 'assertion is *sui generis*', but there appears to be a sense in which the True is also *sui generis* of which the theory is not giving us a complete account[63].

8

It remains to offer some notes on the translation itself.

Unless otherwise indicated, I have used the following renderings:

andeuten	indicate
Anzahl	Number
ausdrücken	express
bedeuten	denote
Bedeutung	denotation
bedeutungsvoll (attributive)	denoting
[*ist*] *bedeutungsvoll* (predicative)	succeeds in denoting
Begriff	concept
Begriffsschrift	Begriffsschrift
behaupten	assert
Behauptung	assertion
beiderseits eindeutig	one-one
besagen	assert
Beziehung	relation
eindeutig	many-one

[63] The feeling that there exists an unsolved difficulty at this point does not seem to be widely shared; but Dummett's paper, just cited, evinces an appreciation of it. Perhaps there is also a hint in Gödel's essay, "Russell's Mathematical Logic", in Schilpp (ed.), *The Philosophy of Bertrand Russell* (New York, 1944), at pp. 129-130.

Erfülltsein [*der Begriffe*]	realization [of concepts]
Function	function
Gegenstand	object
Gleichung	equation, identity
gleichzahlig	equinumerate
Gleichzahligkeit	equinumeracy
Klasse	class
Menge	set
Merkmal	characteristic mark
objectiv	objective
Relation	extension of a relation
sagen	say, assert
Satz	proposition
Sinn	sense
Stufe	level
Umfang	extension
Urtheil	judgment
vertreten (of small Greek consonants)	be a proxy for
vertreten (of courses-of-values)	represent
Wendung	contraposition
Werthverlauf	course-of-values
Zahl	number
zugehörig[*e Function*]	corresponding [function]

A few of these renderings require comment.

Anzahl (Number) is the cardinality of the extension of a concept; *Zahl* (number) is real number. The following passage is apposite:

> Since the Numbers (*Anzahlen*) are not proportions, we must distinguish them from the positive whole numbers (*Zahlen*). Hence it is not possible to enlarge the realm of Numbers to that of the real numbers; they are wholly disjoint realms. The Numbers give the answer to the question, "How many objects are there of a given kind?", whereas the real numbers may be regarded as numbers giving a measure, stating how great a magnitude is as compared with a unit magnitude. Many readers may have been surprised by our formula "$a \cap (b \cap f)$", expecting "$a + 1 = b$" instead; but the f-relation of a Number to its immediate successor is different from the relation $\xi + 1 = \zeta$. The

former holds only between Numbers; the latter is not even confined to the positive whole numbers, so that we can be conducted by means of its converse from the positive whole numbers back over zero and arrive at the negative numbers, whereas a retrogression backward past the Number Ɋ is not possible. (We could not have introduced the plus-sign at any such earlier point without defining it incompletely and piecemeal, thus violating our first principle of definition.) Accordingly, we also distinguish the Numbers Ɋ and 1̵ from the numbers 0 and 1 (*Grundgesetze*, Vol. II, pp. 155 f.).

The device of the capital "N" in "Number" for "*Anzahl*" is borrowed from Austin's translation of *Grundlagen*, p. 2e.

"Begriffsschrift" (literally, "concept-writing") is taken over directly because it is not only a word for a notation (in which case "symbolism" or "ideography" might have served), but also the name of a particular system of logic; not only a formalism, but a formalism together with a particular and distinctive semantical interpretation. Sometimes Frege uses it to mean only a notation, but more frequently in the more specific sense. Rather than translate (e.g.) "symbolism" in the one case and (e.g.) "system of logic" in the other, I have opted for uniformity.

It should be observed that the German words rendered "object" and "objective" are not connected in etymology or in Frege's mind. Concepts are fundamentally different from *objects*; but they are *objective*, i.e., not subjective or private to a particular thinker[64].

"*Relation*" is introduced for "*Umfang einer Beziehung*" in Volume II of *Grundgesetze*[65], in the portion of the book translated here it occurs only in Appendix II dealing with the Russell paradox.

The rendering of "*Satz*" presents great difficulties. In various contexts it can mean sentence, theorem, proposition, clause. In some of Frege's other writings (of 1891 and later) he uses it for that variety of expression (name) which, for him, denotes a truth-value; in such cases "sentence" would be appropriate. In this work, however, "*Satz*" is almost without exception applied

---

[64]I am indebted to Geach and Black, p. ix, for this way of phrasing the distinction.

[65]P. 160.

to expressions *with a judgment-stroke prefixed*, and (as we saw in **7**) such expressions, for Frege, are *not* names. "Assertion" might then be considered, yet it seems that *"Satz"* ought to be rendered differently from *"Behauptung"*. "Theorem" is ruled out as both too wide and too narrow: too narrow because Frege applies *"Satz"* quite generally, and not merely to theorems of his logical theory; too wide because, for example, in his discussion of the Russell paradox where he shows that a self-contradictory statement can in fact be derived from the axioms, Frege gives the derivation informally and does *not* prefix the suspect expressions with the judgment-stroke, apparently on the ground that although they are indeed (unhappily) theorems, he does not believe that they are *true*. Thus we are forced onto "proposition". Some later writers have used this word for the *sense* expressed by a sentence, Frege's *Gedanke*. Therefore the reader must take care here to understand "proposition" in something nearer to its vague English meaning of "a propounding". The situation is unsatisfactory, but Frege has left the translator little choice.

"Lehrsatz" may, however, be rendered "theorem".

"Werthverlauf" is rendered "course-of-values", rather than "range" or "value-range", because the word "range" has an established English usage different from Frege's use of *"Werthverlauf"*. The range of a function F is said to be the class of objects y such that there is an object x such that $F(x) = y$. But the *Werthverlauf* of a function F is most nearly represented in class terminology as the class of ordered couples $x;y$ such that $F(x) = y$.[66] Hence a different English word must be chosen for *"Werthverlauf"*.

A word must be said about the typefaces, since distinctions of typeface are an essential part of the symbolism. After unrecallable arrangements had been made for composing the book, it proved that Gothic letters (Frege's *deutsche Buchstaben*) were not available; the nearest available face was script letters "a", "f", etc., which accordingly have been used instead. Therefore where the words "Gothic letters" occur in the text, they must be understood as referring to script letters. The reader must also take care not to confuse the lower-case Greek alpha

---

[66] Cf. above, **6**. The representation in class terminology is only approximate.

"*a*" with the lower-case Roman "*a*", for example at such places as the definition on p. 92.

Frege's practice is to use displayed text for clarity when appropriate, but not autonymously; the use of quotation marks to signalize the mention as opposed to the use of expressions applies to displayed as well as to running text. I have followed him in this, and in general have used double quotation marks in mentioning expressions. I have used single quotation marks in the sense of 'scare-quotes', as illustrated in the present sentence. Page-references within the compass of what is translated here have been tacitly altered to the present pagination; other references remain unchanged.

Small slips and misprints have been corrected. Where possible the correction has been indicated by the use of square brackets; a list of corrections not accounted for in this way will be found at the end of the volume.

In the text, Frege's footnotes are numbered; the editor's are marked by asterisks.

Finally, mention should be made of previous translations partially overlapping the present one. A translation of most of the author's Introduction and §§0-7 of the first volume of *Grundgesetze* was made by P. E. B. Jourdain and J. Stachelroth and published in three installments in *The Monist* between 1915 and 1917; Geach and Black took over a portion of this version with some modifications in their subsequent anthology, cited in the bibliography below. This translation is not of good quality and the corresponding portions in the present version are wholly fresh. Also in Geach and Black is Geach's translation of parts of Frege's epilogue to the second volume, which is translated here *in toto* as Appendix II. Although much superior to the other extract, Geach's version was ill-suited for inclusion here in not being complete, and also in its omission of all of Frege's symbolism, the formulas being supplanted by Geach's renderings of them into English words. Accordingly this too has been done afresh, although I have sometimes followed Geach's phraseology where I could. The rest of the material here translated, amounting to about seventy percent of the total, has never previously been done into English.

Los Angeles, August, 1964

Montgomery Furth

lvii

Two collections of Frege's essays have appeared:

Translations from the Philosophical Writings of Gottlob Frege, edited by Peter Geach and Max Black. Oxford: Basil Blackwell, 1952; 2d ed. (with corrections), 1960.

Funktion, Begriff, Bedeutung: Fünf logische Studien von Gottlob Frege, herausgegeben und eingeleitet von Günther Patzig. Göttingen: Vandenhoeck und Ruprecht, 1962.

Works by Frege cited in the Editor's Introduction, including subsequent reprintings and English translations, are as follows, in chronological order of original publication:

Begriffsschrift, eine der arithmetischen nachgebildete Formelsprache des reinen Denkens. Halle a/S., 1879; reprinted with supplements, Hildesheim: Georg Olms Verlagsbuchhandlung, 1964. Translation of a portion is in Geach and Black. Translation also announced in J. van Heijenoort, ed., *Source Book in Mathematical Logic, 1879-1931*, Cambridge, Mass.: Harvard University Press, 1964.

Die Grundlagen der Arithmetik. Breslau: Verlag Wilhelm Koebner, 1884. Reprinted at Breslau: Verlag M. & H. Marcus, 1934, and at Hildesheim: Georg Olms Verlagsbuchhandlung, 1961. An English translation, *The Foundations of Arithmetic*, was made by J. L. Austin and published with the German text on facing pages (Oxford: Basil Blackwell, 2d rev. ed., 1953). An edition of the English version alone has appeared (New York: Harper Torchbooks, 1960).

Function und Begriff. An address to the Jenaische Gesellschaft für Medizin und Naturwissenschaft, published at Jena, 1891. Reprinted in Patzig, translation in Geach and Black.

"Über Sinn und Bedeutung," *Zeitschrift für Philosophie und philosophische Kritik*, 100 (1892), 25-50. Reprinted in Patzig, English translations in Geach and Black and also in Feigl and Sellars, eds., *Readings in Philosophical Analysis* (New York: Appleton-Century-Crofts, 1949).

"Über Begriff und Gegenstand," *Vierteljahrsschrift für wissenschaftliche Philosophie*, 16 (1892), 192-205. Reprinted in Patzig, English translation in Geach and Black.

Grundgesetze der Arithmetik, begriffsschriftlich abgeleitet. Band I. Jena: Verlag Hermann Pohle, 1893. Reprinted at Hildesheim: Georg Olms Verlagsbuchhandlung, 1962. (For translations, cf. **8.**)

Review of Husserl's *Philosophie der Arithmetik*, Band I. *Zeitschrift für Philosophie und philosophische Kritik*, 103 (1894), 313-332. Extracts translated in Geach and Black.

"Kritische Beleuchtung einiger Punkte in E. Schröders *Vorlesungen über die Algebra der Logik*". *Archiv für systematische Philosophie*, vol. 1 (1895), pp. 433-456. English translation in Geach and Black.

Grundgesetze der Arithmetik, begriffsschriftlich abgeleitet. Band II. Jena: Verlag Hermann Pohle, 1903. Reprinted at Hildesheim: Georg Olms Verlagsbuchhandlung, 1962. Extracts translated in Geach and Black.

"Der Gedanke," *Beiträge zur Philosophie des deutschen Idealismus*, 1 (1918-1919), 58-77. English translation by A. M. and Marcelle Quinton in *Mind*, 65 (1956), 289-311.

"Die Verneinung," *Beiträge zur Philosophie des deutschen Idealismus*, 1 (1918-1919), 143-157. English translation in Geach and Black.

"Gedankengefüge," *Beiträge zur Philosophie des deutschen Idealismus*, 3 (1923-1926), 36-51. English translation by R. H. Stoothoff in *Mind*, 72 (1963), 1-17.

CONTENTS

INTRODUCTION

v In this book there are to be found theorems upon which arithmetic is based, proved by the use of symbols, which collectively I call Begriffsschrift. The most important of these propositions are collected at the end, some with translation appended. It will be seen that negative, fractional, irrational, and complex numbers have still been left out of account, as have addition, multiplication, and so on. Even the propositions concerning Numbers are still not present with the completeness originally planned; in particular, the proposition is still lacking that the Number of objects falling under a concept is finite if the Number of objects that fall under a superordinated concept is finite. External circumstances have caused me to reserve this, as well as the treatment of other numbers and of the arithmetical operations, for a later installment whose appearance will depend upon the reception accorded this first volume. What I have offered here may be sufficient to give an idea of my method. It might be thought that the propositions concerning the Number 'Infinite'[1] could have been omitted; to be sure, they are not necessary for the foundation of arithmetic in its traditional compass, but their derivation is for the most part simpler than that of the corresponding propositions for finite Numbers and can serve as preparation for it. Other propositions occur which do not treat of Numbers, but which are needed for the proofs; they treat, for example, of following in a series, of the many-oneness of relations, of relative products and of 'coupled' relations, of mapping by means of relations, and the like. Perhaps one might assign these propositions to an enlarged theory of combination.

The proofs are entirely contained in the paragraphs entitled "Construction", whereas the paragraphs entitled "Analysis" are meant to facilitate understanding by providing rough preliminary outlines of the proofs that follow them. The proofs

---

[1]Number of a denumerably infinite set.

1

themselves contain no words but are carried out entirely in my symbols; they appear as sequences of formulas separated by solid or broken lines or other signs. Each of these formulas is a complete proposition including all of the conditions necessary to its validity. This completeness, not permitting the tacit attachment of presuppositions in thought, seems to me indispensable for the rigor of the conduct of proof.

The advance from one proposition to the next takes place according to the Rules summarized in §48, and no transition occurs that is not in accordance with these Rules. How, and by what Rule, an inference is made is indicated by the sign between the formulas, while the sign ——•—— terminates a chain of inference. Here there have to be propositions that are not derived from other propositions; such are in part the Basic Laws summarized in §47, and in part the Definitions collected in a table at the end of the volume with indication of the points at which they first occur. The need of definitions never ceases to be apparent in any attempt of this sort. The principles that must govern the giving of definitions are set out in §33. The definitions do not really create anything, and in my opinion may not do so; they merely introduce abbreviated notations (names), which could be dispensed with were it not that lengthiness would then make for insuperable external difficulties.

The ideal of a strictly scientific method in mathematics, which I have here attempted to realize, and which might indeed be named after Euclid, I should like to describe as follows. It cannot be demanded that everything be proved, because that is impossible; but we can require that all propositions used without proof be expressly declared as such, so that we can see distinctly what the whole structure rests upon. After that we must try to diminish the number of these primitive laws as far as possible, by proving everything that can be proved. Furthermore, I demand—and in this I go beyond Euclid—that all methods of inference employed be specified in advance; otherwise we cannot be certain of satisfying the first requirement. This ideal I believe I have now essentially attained. Only in a few points could one be any more exacting. So as to secure more flexibility and avoid extravagant length I have allowed myself to make tacit use of the interchangeability of subcomponents (conditions) and of the possibility of amalgamating identical

2

subcomponents, and have not reduced the methods of inference to the smallest possible number. Readers of my *Begriffsschrift* will be able to gather from it the way in which here too the strictest requirements could be satisfied, but likewise, that this would entail a considerable increase in volume.

Apart from this, I believe, the only criticisms that can justly be made against this book concern not the rigor but merely the choice of the course of proof and of intermediate steps. Frequently several routes for a proof are open; I have not tried to travel them all, and thus it is possible—even probable—that I have not invariably chosen the shortest. Let him who finds fault in this respect do better himself. Other matters will be disputable. Some might perhaps have preferred me to draw the limits of the permissible methods of inference more widely, thus attaining greater flexibility and brevity. But we must call a halt at some point, if the ideal which I have set is approved of at all—and wherever we do so, people can always say: it would have been better if more methods of inference had been permitted.

Because there are no gaps in the chains of inference, every 'axiom', every 'assumption', 'hypothesis', or whatever you wish to call it, upon which a proof is based is brought to light; and in this way we gain a basis upon which to judge the epistemological nature of the law that is proved. Of course the pronouncement is often made that arithmetic is merely a more highly developed logic; yet that remains disputable so long as transitions occur in the proofs that are not made according to acknowledged laws of logic, but seem rather to be based upon something known by intuition. Only if these transitions are split up into logically simple steps can we be persuaded that the root of the matter is logic alone. I have drawn together everything that can facilitate a judgment as to whether the chains of inference are cohesive and the buttresses solid. If anyone should find anything defective, he must be able to state precisely where, according to him, the error lies: in the Basic Laws, in the Definitions, in the Rules, or in the application of the Rules at a definite point. If we find everything in order, then we have accurate knowledge of the grounds upon which each individual theorem is based. A dispute can arise, so far as I can see, only with regard to my Basic Law concerning courses-of-values

(V), which logicians perhaps have not yet expressly enunciated, and yet is what people have in mind, for example, where they speak of the extensions of concepts. I hold that it is a law of pure logic. In any event the place is pointed out where the decision must be made.

My purpose necessitates many departures from what is customary in mathematics. The requirements upon the rigor of proof inevitably entail greater length; anyone not bearing this in mind will indeed be surprised at how laboriously a proposition is often proved here that he believes he can grasp in one single act of understanding. This will strike us particularly if we compare Herr Dedekind's work *Was sind und was sollen die Zahlen?*, the most thoroughgoing work on the foundations of arithmetic that has lately come to my notice. In much less space it pursues the laws of arithmetic much farther than is done here. To be sure, this brevity is attained only because a great deal is really not proved at all. Frequently Herr Dedekind merely says that the proof follows from such and such propositions; he makes use of dots, as in the expression "$\mathfrak{M}(A, B, C, \cdots)$"; an inventory of the logical or other laws taken by him as basic is nowhere to be found, and even if it were, there would be no way of telling whether no others were actually used; for that to be possible the proofs would have to be not merely indicated but carried out, without gaps. Herr Dedekind, like myself, is of the opinion that the theory of numbers is a part of logic; but his work hardly contributes to its confirmation, because the expressions "system" and "a thing belongs to a thing", which he uses, are not usual in logic and are not reduced to acknowledged logical notions. I do not say this as a reproach, for his procedure may have been the most appropriate for his purpose; I say it only to set my intention in a clearer light by contrast. The length of a proof ought not to be measured by the yard. It is easy to make a proof look short on paper by skipping over many intermediate links in the chain of inference and merely indicating large parts of it. Generally people are satisfied if every step in the proof is evidently correct, and this is permissible if one merely wishes to be persuaded that the proposition to be proved is true. But if it is a matter of gaining an insight into the nature of this 'being evident', this procedure does not suffice; we must put down all of the intermediate steps, that the

4

full light of consciousness may fall upon them. Mathematicians
generally are indeed only concerned with the content of a proposition and with the fact that it is to be proved. What is new in
this book is not the content of the proposition, but the way in
which the proof is carried out and the foundations on which it
rests. That this essentially different viewpoint calls for a different method of treatment should not surprise us. If one of our
propositions is derived in the customary way some proposition
will easily be overlooked which does not seem necessary to the
proof; yet careful pondering of my proof will, I believe, show
the proposition to be indispensable unless some quite different
route is taken. Then again, in one or another of our propositions conditions may be found that first strike one as unnecessary, but that turn out either to be necessary after all, or to be
dispensable only by means of a proposition that must be especially proved for the purpose.

With this book I carry out a design that I had in view as early
as my *Begriffsschrift* of 1879 and announced in my *Grundlagen
der Arithmetik* of 1884[2]. I wish here to substantiate in actual
x practice the view of Number that I expounded in the latter book.
The most fundamental of my results I expressed there, in §46,
by saying that a statement of number expresses an assertion
about a concept; and the present account rests upon this. If
anyone is of another view, let him try, using symbols, to base
upon his view an account both consistent and practicable, and
he will see that it does not work. In ordinary language, to be
sure, the situation is not so transparent; but if we attend with
sufficient care we find that here, too, in a statement of number
there is invariably mention of a concept—not a group, or an aggregate, or the like—or that, if a group or aggregate is mentioned,
it is invariably determined by a concept, that is, by the properties an object must have in order to belong to the group; while
what makes the group into a group, or a system into a system—
the relations of the members to one another—is for the Number
wholly irrelevant.

One reason why the execution appears so long after the an-
nouncement is to be found in internal changes in my Begriffsschrift, which forced me to discard an almost completed

---

[2]Cf. the Introduction and §§90 and 91 of my *Grundlagen der Arithmetik*, Breslau, Verlag Wilhelm Koebner, 1884.

manuscript. These improvements may be mentioned here briefly. The primitive signs used in *Begriffsschrift* occur here also, with one exception. Instead of the three parallel lines I have adopted the ordinary sign of equality, since I have persuaded myself that it has in arithmetic precisely the meaning that I wish to symbolize. That is, I use the word "equal"* to mean the same as "coinciding with" or "identical with"; and the sign of equality is actually used in arithmetic in this way. The opposition that may arise against this will very likely rest on an inadequate distinction between sign and thing signified. Of course in the equation "$2^2 = 2+2$" the sign on the left is different from that on the right; but both designate or denote the same number[3]. To the old primitive signs two more have now been added: the smooth breathing, for the notation for the course-of-values of a function, and a sign meant to do the work of the definite article of everyday language. The introduction of the courses-of-values of functions is a vital advance, thanks to which we gain far greater flexibility. The former derivative signs can now be replaced by other, simpler ones, although the definitions of the many-oneness of a relation, of following in a series, and of a mapping, are essentially the same as those which I gave in part in *Begriffsschrift* and in part in *Grundlagen der Arithmetik*. But the courses-of-values are also extremely x important in principle; in fact, I define Number itself as the extension of a concept, and extensions of concepts are by my definitions courses-of-values. Thus we just cannot get on without them. The old signs that appear here outwardly unchanged, and whose algorithm has also hardly changed, are nonetheless provided with different explanations. The former 'content-stroke' reappears as the 'horizontal'. These are consequences of a thoroughgoing development of my logical views. Formerly I distinguished two components in that whose external form is a declarative sentence: (1) the acknowledgment of truth, (2) the content that is acknowledged to be true. The content I called a 'possible content of judgment'. This last has now split for

---

**gleich.*

[3] I also say: the sense of the sign on the right side is different from that of the sign on the left; but the denotation is the same. Cf. my essay on sense and denotation in the *Zeitschrift für Philosophie und philosophische Kritik*, vol. 100, p. 25.

me into what I call 'thought' and 'truth-value', as a consequence of distinguishing between sense and denotation of a sign. In this case the sense of a sentence is a thought, and its denotation a truth-value. Over and above this is the acknowledgment that the truth-value is the True. That is, I distinguish two truth-values: the True and the False. I have justified this more thoroughly in my essay on sense and denotation, mentioned above; here it may merely be mentioned that only in this way can indirect discourse be correctly understood. That is, the thought, which otherwise is the sense of a sentence, in indirect discourse becomes its denotation. How much simpler and sharper everything becomes by the introduction of truth-values, only detailed acquaintance with this book can show. These advantages alone put a great weight in the balance in favor of my own conception, which indeed may seem strange at first sight. Also the nature of the function, as distinguished from the object, is characterized more sharply here than in *Begriffsschrift*. From this results further the distinction between first- and second-level functions. As I have explained in my lecture *Function und Begriff*[4], concepts and relations are 'functions' in my extended meaning of the term; and so we have to distinguish first- and second-level concepts, equal-leveled and unequal-leveled relations.

It will be seen that the years have not passed in vain since the appearance of my *Begriffsschrift* and *Grundlagen*: they have brought the work to maturity. But just that which I recognize as a vital advance stands, as I cannot conceal from myself, as a great obstacle in the way of the dissemination and the effectiveness of my book. And that which is not its least value, the rigorous avoidance of gaps in the chains of inference, will, I fear, win it little thanks. I have moved farther away from the accepted conceptions, and have thereby stamped my views with an impress of paradox. An expression cropping up here or there, as one leafs through these pages, may easily appear strange and create prejudice. I myself can estimate to some extent the resistance with which my innovations will be met, because I had first to overcome something similar in myself in order to make them. For I have not arrived at them haphazardly or out of a craving for novelty, but was driven by the nature of the

xi

[4]Jena, Verlag Hermann Pohle, 1891.

case.

With this I arrive at the second reason for my delay: the discouragement that overcame me at times because of the cool reception—or more accurately the lack of reception—accorded by mathematicians to the writings of mine that I have mentioned[5], and because of the unpropitious currents in scientific thought against which my book will have to struggle. Even the first impression must frighten people off: unfamiliar signs, pages of nothing but alien-looking formulas. And so at times I turned to other subjects. But I could not keep the results of my thinking, which seemed valuable to me myself, locked up in my desk for long, and the labor already expended kept requiring new labor so as not to be in vain. So the subject did not let me go. In a case of this kind, where the value of a book cannot be recognized by a quick reading, criticism ought to step in with assistance. But criticism is in general too poorly remunerated. A critic can never hope to be repaid in cash for the toil that a deep study of this book sets before him. My only remaining hope is that someone may have enough confidence in the matter beforehand to expect in the intellectual profit a sufficient reward, and that he will make public the outcome of his careful examination. Not that only a laudatory review could satisfy me; on the contrary, I should far prefer an attack that is thoroughly well-informed than a commendation in general terms not touching the root of the matter. I should like to facilitate the work of the reader who approaches the book with such purposes by means of a few hints.

So as to gain at the outset a rough idea of the way in which I express thoughts with my signs, it will be useful to consider more closely some of the simpler theorems in the Table of More Important Theorems to which a translation is appended. One will then be able to conjecture what other theorems, similar to these but not followed by translation, are intended to assert. After that one may begin with paragraph §0 and set about mastering the Exposition of the Begriffsschrift. But my advice is to begin by acquainting oneself with it rapidly and not to

---

[5]In vain do we seek [notice of] my *Grundlagen der Arithmetik* in the *Jahrbuch über die Fortschritte der Mathematik*. Researchers in the same area, Dedekind, Otto Stolz, von Helmholtz, seem not to be aware of my works. And Kronecker fails to mention them in his essay on the concept of number.

delay too long over the discussions of details. Some matters had to be taken up in order to be able to meet all objections, but are nevertheless inessential to an understanding of the propositions of Begriffsschrift. I count among these the second half of §8, beginning on p. 42 with the words "If we now set up"; also the second half of §9, beginning on p. 44 with the words "If I say generally"; and the whole of §10. These portions may be skipped entirely on a first reading. The same holds for §§26 and 28 through 31. On the other hand I should like to stress as especially important for comprehension the first half of §8, and also §§12 and 13. A more exact reading may begin with §34 and continue to the end; one will have to return occasionally to the §§ previously only skimmed, and this will be made easier by the index at the end and the Table of Contents. The derivations in §§49 to 52 can serve as preparation for understanding the proofs themselves. All of the methods of inference and practically all of the applications of our Basic Laws already occur there. After one has reached the end in this way, he may reread the Exposition of the Begriffsschrift as a connected whole, keeping in mind that the stipulations that are not made use of later and hence seem superfluous serve to carry out the basic principle that every correctly-formed name is to denote something, a principle that is essential for full rigor. In this way, I believe, the suspicion that may at first be aroused by my innovations will gradually be dispelled. The reader will recognize that my basic principles at no point lead to consequences that he is not himself forced to acknowledge as correct. Perhaps then he will also grant that at the outset he overrated the labor involved, that my gapless procedure even facilitates understanding, once the obstacle of the novelty of the signs is overcome. May I be so fortunate as to find such a reader and judge! for a notice based on superficial perusal can easily do more harm than good.

Otherwise the prospects of my book are of course slight. In any event I must relinquish as readers all those mathematicians who, if they bump into logical expressions such as "concept", "relation", "judgment", think: *metaphysica sunt, non leguntur,* and likewise those philosophers who at the sight of a formula cry: *mathematica sunt, non leguntur*; and the number of such persons is surely not small. Perhaps the number of mathematicians who trouble themselves over the foundation of their science is not great, and even these frequently seem to be in a great hurry until they have got the fundamental principles behind them. And I scarcely dare hope that my reasons for painstaking rigor and its inevitable lengthiness will persuade many of them. But what once becomes established has great power over men's minds. If I compare arithmetic with a tree that unfolds upward into a multitude of techniques and theorems while its root drives into the depths, then it seems to me that the impetus of the root, at least in Germany, is rather weak. Even in a work that we should like to count as tending in the latter direction, the *Algebra der Logik* of E. Schröder, the top-growth quickly gains the upper hand even before any great depth has been reached, the effect being a bending upward and an unfolding into techniques and theorems.

Also unpropitious for my book is the widespread inclination to acknowledge as existing only what can be perceived by the senses. That which cannot, people try to deny or else to ignore. Now the objects of arithmetic, i.e., numbers, cannot be perceived by the senses. How do we come to terms with them? Simplicity itself! We pronounce the numerical signs to be the numbers. Then in the signs we have something visible, and that is naturally the chief thing. Of course the signs have totally different properties from the numbers themselves, but what does that matter? We simply invest them with the properties we wish by so-called 'definitions'. Of course it is a puzzle how there can be a definition where no question is raised about the connection between sign and thing signified. So far as possible we knead sign and thing signified indistinguishably together; and then we can make assertions of existence on the basis of tangibility[6], or then again bring to the fore the true properties of numbers, as the occasion requires. Sometimes, it seems, the numerical signs are regarded as chess pieces and the so-called 'definitions' as rules of the game. The sign then does not designate anything: it is the subject matter itself. To be sure, in all this one trifling detail is overlooked: namely, that with

[6] Cf. E. Heine, *Die Elemente der Functionslehre*, in Crelle's *Journal*, vol. 74, p. 173: "As for definition, I adopt the purely formalistic standpoint; what I call numbers are certain tangible signs, so that the existence of these numbers is thus unquestionable."

"$3^2 + 4^2 = 5^2$" we express a thought, whereas a configuration of chess pieces asserts nothing. Where people are satisfied with such superficialities, of course there is no basis for any deeper understanding.

It is important that we make clear at this point what definition is and what can be attained by means of it. It seems frequently to be credited with a creative power; but all it accomplishes is that something is marked out in sharp relief and designated by a name. Just as the geographer does not create a sea when he draws boundary lines and says: the part of the ocean's surface bounded by these lines I am going to call the Yellow Sea, so too the mathematician cannot really create anything by his defining. Nor can one by pure definition magically conjure into a thing a property that in fact it does not possess—save that of now being called by the name with which one has named it. But that an oval figure produced on paper with ink should by a definition acquire the property of yielding one when added to one, I can only regard as a scientific superstition. One could just as well by a pure definition make a lazy pupil diligent. It is easy for unclarity to arise here if we do not distinguish sufficiently between concept and object. If we say: 'a square is a rectangle in which the adjacent sides are equal', we define the concept *square* by specifying what properties a thing must have in order to fall under this concept. These properties I call 'characteristic marks' of the concept. But these characteristic marks of a concept, properly understood, are not the same as its properties. The concept *square* is not a rectangle; only such objects as may fall under this concept are rectangles, just as the concept *black cloth* is neither black nor a cloth. Whether there are any such objects is not known immediately from the definition. Now suppose one defines, for instance, the number zero, by saying: it is something which yields one when added to one. In so doing one has defined a concept, by specifying what property an object must have in order to fall under the concept. But this property is not a property of the concept defined. People frequently seem to fancy that by the definition something has been created that yields one when added to one. A great delusion! The concept defined does not possess this property, nor is the definition any guarantee that the concept is realized—a matter requiring separate investigation. Only when

11

we have proved that there exists at least and at most one object with the required property are we in a position to invest this object with the proper name "zero". To create zero is consequently impossible. I have already repeatedly explained these things, but apparently without effect[7].

From the prevailing logic, too, I cannot hope for any understanding of my distinction between a characteristic mark of a concept and a property of an object[8]; for it seems to be infected through and through with psychology. If people consider, instead of things themselves, only their subjective *simulacra*, their ideas of them, then naturally all the more delicate distinctions within the subject matter are lost, and others appear in their place that are logically completely worthless. And this brings me to what stands in the way of the influence of my book among logicians: namely, the corrupting incursion of psychology into logic. Our conception of the laws of logic is necessarily decisive for our treatment of the science of logic, and that conception in turn is connected with our understanding of the word xv "true". It will be granted by all at the outset that the laws of logic ought to be guiding principles for thought in the attainment of truth, yet this is only too easily forgotten, and here what is fatal is the double meaning of the word "law". In one sense a law asserts what is; in the other it prescribes what ought to be. Only in the latter sense can the laws of logic be called 'laws of thought': so far as they stipulate the way in which one ought to think. Any law asserting what is, can be conceived as prescribing that one ought to think in conformity with it, and is thus in that sense a law of thought. This holds for laws of geometry and physics no less than for laws of logic. The latter have a special title to the name "laws of thought" only if we mean to assert that they are the most general laws, which prescribe universally the way in which one ought to think if one is to think at all. But the expression "law of thought" seduces us into supposing that these laws govern thinking in the same way as laws of nature govern events in the external world. In that case they can be nothing but laws of psychology:

---

[7]Mathematicians reluctant to venture into the labyrinths of philosophy are requested to leave off reading the Introduction at this point.

[8]In the *Logik* of Herr B. Erdmann I find no trace of this important distinction.

12

for thinking is a mental process. And if logic were concerned with these psychological laws it would be a part of psychology; it is in fact viewed in just this way. These laws of thought can in that case be regarded as guiding principles in the sense that they give an average, like statements about 'how it is that good digestion occurs in man', or 'how one speaks grammatically', or 'how one dresses fashionably'. Then one can only say: men's taking something to be true conforms on the average to these laws, at present and relative to our knowledge of men; thus if one wishes to correspond with the average one will conform to these. But just as what is fashionable in dress at the moment will shortly be fashionable no longer and among the Chinese is not fashionable now, so these psychological laws of thought can be laid down only with restrictions on their authority. Of course—if logic has to do with something's being taken to be true, rather than with its being true! And these are what the psychological logicians confuse. Thus Herr B. Erdmann in the first volume of his *Logik*[9] (pp. 272-275) equates truth with 'general validity', and bases this upon 'general certainty regarding the object of judgment', and bases this in turn upon 'general agreement among the subjects who judge'. Thus in the end truth is reduced to individuals' taking something to be true. All I have to say to this is: being true is different from being taken to be true, whether by one or many or everybody, and in no case is to be reduced to it. There is no contradiction in something's being true which everybody takes to be false. I understand by 'laws of logic' not psychological laws of takings-to-be-true, but laws of truth. If it is true that I am writing this in my chamber on the 13th of July, 1893, while the wind howls out-of-doors, then it remains true even if all men should subsequently take it to be false. If being true is thus independent of being acknowledged by somebody or other, then the laws of truth are not psychological laws: they are boundary stones set in an eternal foundation, which our thought can overflow, but never displace. It is because of this that they have authority for our thought if it would attain to truth. They do not bear the relation to thought that the laws of grammar bear to language; they do not make explicit the nature of our human thinking and change as it changes. Of course, Herr Erdmann's conception of the laws of logic is

[9]Halle a. S., Max Niemeyer, 1892.

quite different. He doubts their unconditional and eternal validity and would restrict them to our thought as it is now (pp. 375 ff.). "Our thought" surely can only mean the thought of human beings up to the present. Accordingly the possibility remains of men or other beings being discovered who were capable of bringing off judgments contradicting our laws of logic. If this were to happen? Herr Erdmann would say: here we see that these principles do not hold generally. Certainly!—if these are psychological laws, their verbal expression must single out the family of beings whose thought is empirically governed by them. I should say: thus there exist beings that recognize certain truths not as we do, immediately, but perhaps led by some lengthier route of induction. But what if beings were even found whose laws of thought flatly contradicted ours and therefore frequently led to contrary results even in practice? The psychological logician could only acknowledge the fact and say simply: those laws hold for them, these laws hold for us. I should say: we have here a hitherto unknown type of madness. Anyone who understands laws of logic to be laws that prescribe the way in which one ought to think—to be laws of truth, and not natural laws of human beings' taking a thing to be true—will ask, who is right? Whose laws of taking-to-be-true are in accord with the laws of truth? The psychological logician cannot ask this question; if he did he would be recognizing laws of truth that were not laws of psychology. One could scarcely falsify the sense of the word "true" more mischievously than by including in it a reference to the subjects who judge. Someone will now no doubt object that the sentence "I am hungry" can be true for one person and false for another. The sentence, certainly—but not the thought; for the word "I" in the mouth of the other person denotes a different man, and hence the sentence xv uttered by the other person expresses a different thought. All determinations of the place, the time, and the like, belong to the thought whose truth is in point; its truth itself is independent of place or time. How, then, is the Principle of Identity really to be read? Like this, for instance: "It is impossible for people in the year 1893 to acknowledge an object as being different from itself"? Or like this: "Every object is identical with itself"? The former law concerns human beings and contains a temporal reference; in the latter there is no talk either of human beings or of time. The latter is a law of truth, the former a law of people's taking-to-be-true. The content of the two is wholly different and they are independent of one another; neither can be inferred from the other. Hence it is extremely confusing to designate both by the same name, "Principle of Identity". These mixings-together of wholly different things are to blame for the frightful unclarity that we encounter among the psychological logicians.

The question why and with what right we acknowledge a law of logic to be true, logic can answer only by reducing it to another law of logic. Where that is not possible, logic can give no answer. If we step away from logic, we may say: we are compelled to make judgments by our own nature and by external circumstances; and if we do so, we cannot reject this law—of Identity, for example; we must acknowledge it unless we wish to reduce our thought to confusion and finally renounce all judgment whatever. I shall neither dispute nor support this view; I shall merely remark that what we have here is not a logical consequence. What is given is not a reason for something's being true, but for our taking it to be true. Not only that: this impossibility of our rejecting the law in question hinders us not at all in supposing beings who do reject it; where it hinders us is in supposing that these beings are right in so doing, it hinders us in having doubts whether we or they are right. At least this is true of myself. If other persons presume to acknowledge and doubt a law in the same breath, it seems to me an attempt to jump out of one's own skin against which I can do no more than urgently warn them. Anyone who has once acknowledged a law of truth has by the same token acknowledged a law that prescribes the way in which one ought to judge, no matter where, or when, or by whom the judgment is made.

Surveying the whole question, it seems to me that the source of the dispute lies in a difference in our conceptions of what is true. For me, what is true is something objective and independent of the judging subject; for psychological logicians it is not. What Herr B. Erdmann calls 'objective certainty' is merely a general acknowledgment on the part of the subjects who judge, which is thus not independent of them but susceptible to alteration with the constitution of their minds.

We can generalize this still further: for me there is a domain of what is objective, which is distinct from that of what is actual, whereas the psychological logicians without ado take what is not actual to be subjective. And yet it is quite impossible to understand why something that has a status independent of the judging subject has to be actual, i.e., has to be capable of acting directly or indirectly on the senses*. No such connection is to be found between the concepts [of being objective and being actual], and we can even adduce examples pointing in the opposite direction. The number one, for instance, is not easily taken to be actual, unless we are disciples of John Stuart Mill. On the other hand, it is impossible to ascribe to every person his own number one; for in that case we should first have to investigate the extent to which the properties of these ones agreed, and if one person said "one times one is one" and the next said "one times one is two", we could only register the difference and say: your one has one property, mine has another. There could be no question of any argument as to who was right, or of any attempt to correct anyone; for they would not be speaking of the same object. Obviously this is totally contrary to the sense of the word "one" and the sense of the sentence "one times one is one". Since the number one, being the same for everyone, stands apart from everyone in the same way**, it can no more be researched by making psychological observations than can the moon. Whatever ideas there may be of the number one in individual souls, they are still to be as carefully distinguished from the number one, as ideas of the moon are to be distinguished from the moon itself. Because the psychological logicians fail to recognize the possibility of there being something objective that is not actual, they take concepts to be ideas and thereby consign them to psychology. But the true state of affairs makes itself felt too forcibly for this to be easily carried through. From this there stems an equivocation on the word "idea": at some times it seems to mean something that belongs to the mental life of an individual and that merges with other ideas with which it is associated, according to the laws of psychology; at other times it seems to mean something standing apart from everyone in the same way, where a possessor of the

---

*The translation reproduces a play upon the expressions *"wirklich"* and *"auf die Sinne wirken"*.

**It is not possible to reproduce in English the implied play upon the expressions *"Gegenstand"* and *"gegenüberstehen"*.

'idea' is neither mentioned nor even tacitly presupposed. These two uses of the word cannot be reconciled; for those associations and mergings occur only within the individual mind whose ideas are involved, and have only to do with something belonging to that mind as idiosyncratically as its pleasure or its pain. We must never forget that different people's ideas, however similar they may be (which, incidentally, we cannot accurately determine), nevertheless do not coincide but have to be distinguished. Every man has his own ideas, which are not those of any other. Here of course I am understanding "idea" in the psychological sense. The equivocation on this word obscures the issue and helps the psychological logicians to conceal their weakness. When will a stop be put to this? In the end everything is drawn into the sphere of psychology; the boundary that separates objective and subjective fades away more and more, and even actual objects themselves are treated psychologically, as ideas. For what else is *actual* but a predicate? and what else are logical predicates but ideas? Thus everything drifts into idealism and from that point with perfect consistency into solipsism. If every man designated something different by the name "moon", namely one of his own ideas, much as he expresses his own pain by the cry "Ouch", then of course the psychological point of view would be justified; but an argument about the properties of the moon would be pointless: one person could perfectly well assert of his moon the opposite of what the other person, with equal right, said of his. If we could not grasp anything but what was within our own selves, then a conflict of opinions [based on] a mutual understanding would be impossible, because a common ground would be lacking, and no idea in the psychological sense can afford us such a ground. There would be no logic to be appointed arbiter in the conflict of opinions.

However, so as to dispel any notion that I am tilting at windmills, I shall demonstrate this helpless foundering in idealism in the case of a definite book. I choose for this the *Logik* of Herr B. Erdmann already mentioned, as one of the most recent works of the psychological school and not likely to be denied all importance. First let us look at the following sentence:

"Thus psychology teaches with certainty that the objects of memory and imagination, as well as those of morbid hallucinatory and delusive ideation, are ideal in their nature.... Ideal as well is the whole realm of mathematical ideas properly so called, from the number-series down to the objects of mechanics (Vol. I, p. 85)."

What an assemblage! The number ten shall thus stand on a level with hallucinations! Obviously what is objective and not actual is being mixed up here with what is subjective. Some objective things are actual, others are not. *Actual* is merely one predicate out of many and has no more special relevance to logic than, e.g., the predicate *algebraic* as asserted of a curve. Of course by this confusion Herr Erdmann becomes entangled in metaphysics, however much he struggles to keep clear of it. I take it as a sure sign of a mistake if logic has need of metaphysics and psychology—sciences that require their own logical first principles. In this case then, where is the ultimate basis upon which everything rests? Or is it like Münchhausen, who pulled himself out of the bog by his own hair? I am pessimistic about that possibility and conjecture that Herr Erdmann is stuck xx in his psychologico-metaphysical bog.

For Herr Erdmann there is no real objectivity; everything is idea. We may be convinced of this by his own statements; thus we read,

"As a relation between what is ideated, the judgment presupposes at least two points of reference between which the relation holds. As an *assertion* about what is ideated it requires that one of these points of reference be determined as the object about which something is asserted, as the subject..., and the second as the object that is asserted, as the predicate... (Vol. I, p. 187)."

We see here first of all that both the subject about which something is asserted and the predicate are marked as 'objects' or 'things ideated'. Instead of "object" he could just as well have said "thing ideated"; for we read,

"For objects are things ideated (Vol. I, p. 81)."

But conversely too, everything ideated is an object:

"According to its origin, the ideated divides on the one hand into objects of sense-perception and of self-consciousness, and on the other hand into original and derived (Vol. I, p. 38)."

What arises from sense-perception and from self-consciousness is certainly mental in nature. The objects, the ideated, and hence subject and predicate as well, are thereby assigned to psychology. This is confirmed by the following passage:

"In general it is either the ideated or the idea, for the two are one and the same: what is ideated is the idea, and the idea is what is ideated (Vol. I, pp. 147-148)."

The word "idea" nowadays is as a rule taken in the psychological sense; that this is Herr Erdmann's use as well, we see from the following passages:

"Consciousness accordingly is the general case of feeling, ideating, willing (Vol. I, p. 35);"

"Ideating is a compound of the *ideas* [in which objects are given us] and *passages of ideas* [by which these ideas are remembered, combined, or predicatively analyzed according to their associative relations] (Vol. I, p. 36)."*

After this, we ought not to be surprised that an object comes into existence in a psychological way:

"To the extent that a mass of perceptions [e.g., the noise of a passing carriage], presents the same thing as have previous stimuli and the excitations triggered by them, it *reproduces* the memory-traces that stem from the sameness of previous stimuli and *amalgamates* with them to form the object of the apperceived idea (Vol. I, p. 42)."

Then on p. 43 it is shown as an example how a steel engraving of Raphael's Sistine Madonna comes into existence in a purely psychological way without steel plate, ink, press, or
xxi paper! After all this there cannot be any doubt that the object about which an assertion is made, the subject, is according to Herr Erdmann's opinion supposed to be an idea in the psychological sense of the word, and likewise for the predicate, the object that is asserted. If this were right it could not be truly asserted of any subject that it was green; for there are no green ideas. Nor could I assert of any subject that it was independent of being ideated, or of myself, who ideates it, any more than my decisions are independent of my willing, or of myself who wills; to the contrary, if I were destroyed they would be destroyed along with me. Thus there is no real objectivity for Herr Erdmann, as follows also from his representing what is ideated or the idea in general, the object in the most general

---

*In this and the following two extracts I have translated some phrases from Erdmann omitted by Frege in citing him.

sense of the word, as *summum genus* (γενικώτατον) (p. 147). And so he is an idealist. If the idealists were consistent, they would put down the sentence "Charlemagne conquered the Saxons" as neither true nor false, but as fiction, just as we are accustomed to regard, for example, the sentence "Nessus carried Deianeira across the river Evenus"; for even the sentence "Nessus did not carry Deianeira across the river Evenus" could be true only if the name "Nessus" had a bearer. It would not be easy to dislodge the idealists from this point of view. But we do not need to put up with their falsification of the sense of the sentence, as if I meant to assert something about my idea when I speak of Charlemagne; I simply mean to designate a man, independent of me and my ideating, and to assert something about him. We may grant the idealists that the attainment of this intention is not completely sure and that, without wishing to, I may perhaps lapse from truth into fiction; but this can change nothing in the sense. With the sentence "This blade of grass is green" I assert nothing about my idea; I am not designating any of my ideas with the words "this blade of grass", and if I were, then the sentence would be false. Here there enters a second falsification, namely that my idea of green is asserted of my idea of this blade of grass. I repeat: in this sentence there is no talk whatever of my ideas; it is the idealists who foist that sense upon us. By the way, I entirely fail to understand how an idea can be asserted of anything. It would be just as much a falsification to say that in the sentence "the moon is independent of myself and my ideating", my idea of independence-of-myself-and-my-ideating was asserted of my idea of the moon; this would be to surrender all objectivity in the proper sense of the word and push something wholly different into its place. Certainly it is possible that in making a judgment such a play of ideas occurs; but that is not the sense of the sentence. It may also be observed that with the same sentence and the same sense of that sentence the play of ideas can be wholly different. And it is this logically irrelevant accompanying phenomenon that our logicians take for the proper object of their study.

As may be seen, the nature of the situation opposes this foundering in idealism, and Herr Erdmann would not like to admit that for him there is no real objectivity; but equally plain is the futility of trying to deny it. For if all subjects and all predicates are ideas and if all thinking is nothing but the creating, connecting, and altering of ideas, then it is impossible to understand how anything objective is ever to be reached. A symptom of this futile struggle is the use of the words "thing ideated" and "object", which at first sight seem intended to designate something objective, as opposed to an idea, though as it turns out they only *seem* so intended and in fact denote that very thing. Well then, why this superfluity of expressions? That is not hard to unriddle. We observe that what is being spoken of is an object of the idea, although the object is supposed to be itself an idea. Thus it would be an idea of an idea. What relation between ideas are we supposed to be designating here? Obscure as this is, it is also readily understandable how, from the opposed workings of the nature of the situation and idealism, such giddy whirlpools can arise. Everywhere here we see the object of which I make an idea for myself being mixed up with this idea, and then the difference between them moving into prominence again. We recognize this conflict also in the following sentence:

"For an idea whose object is general is on that account, as such, as a conscious event, no more general itself than an idea is real because its object is posited as real, or than an object that we perceive as sweet, [brown, warm, triangular, distant], is given by ideas that are themselves sweet, [brown, warm, triangular, distant] (Vol. I, p. 86)."

Here the true situation is forcibly making itself felt. I could almost agree with it. But if we observe that on Erdmann's principles the object of an idea and the object that is given by ideas are themselves ideas, then we see that all struggle is in vain. I request too that the words "as such" not be forgotten; they also occur similarly in this passage:

"Where actuality is asserted of an object, the real subject of this judgment is not the object or the thing ideated as such, but rather the *Transcendent*, which is presupposed as the ground of being of this thing that is ideated and represented in it. The Transcendent is not to be taken here as the unknowable . . . rather its transcendence is to consist only in its independence of being ideated (Vol. I, p. 83)."

Another futile attempt to work himself out of the bog! If we take the words seriously, what is said is that in this case the subject is not an idea. But if this is possible then it is not clear why for other predicates, which indicate particular modes of activity or actuality, the real subject always has to be an idea, e.g., in the judgment "the earth is magnetic". Thus we should arrive at the view that only in a few judgments was the real subject an idea. But if it is once admitted that it is not essential for either the subject or the predicate to be an idea, then the ground is pulled from beneath the feet of the whole psychological logic. All psychological considerations, with which our logic-books of today are swollen, then prove to be irrelevant.

But probably we ought not to take Transcendence in Herr Erdmann's case so seriously. I need only remind him of his own pronouncement:

> " ... the *metaphysical* limit of our ideation, the Transcendent, is also subordinate to the *summum genus* (Vol. I, p. 148),"

and with that he founders; for this *summum genus* (γενικώτατον) is according to him just the ideated or the idea in general. Or was the sense of the word "Transcendent" as used above, supposed to differ from its sense here? One would have thought that in *every* case the Transcendent had to be subordinate to the *summum genus*.

Let us dwell a moment longer on the expression "as such". I shall suppose that somebody wishes me to imagine that all objects are nothing but pictures on my retina. Very well; so far I have no objections. But now he declares further that the tower is bigger than the window through which I suppose that I am seeing it. Now to this I should say: "Either it is not the case that both the tower and the window are pictures on my retina, and then the tower may be bigger than the window; or else the tower and the window are, as you say, pictures on my retina, and then the tower is not bigger, but smaller than the window." It is at this point that he tries to extricate himself from the dilemma with "as such", and he says: "To be sure, the retinal picture of the tower is *as such* not bigger than the retinal picture of the window." At this I almost feel like losing my temper entirely and shouting at him: "Well then, the retinal picture of the tower is not bigger than the retinal picture of the window at all, and if the tower were the retinal picture of the tower and the window were the

22

retinal picture of the window, then the tower would not be bigger than the window either, and if your logic teaches you differently it is absolutely worthless!'' This ''as such'' is a splendid discovery for hazy writers reluctant to say either yes or no. But I will not put up with this hovering between the two; I ask: If actuality is asserted of an object, then is the real subject of the judgment the idea? Yes or no? If it is not, then presumably the subject is the Transcendent, which is presupposed as the ground of being of this idea. But this Transcendent is itself a thing ideated or an idea. Thus we are driven on to the supposition that the subject of the judgment is not the ideated Transcendent, but the Transcendent that is presupposed as the ground of being of this ideated Transcendent. Thus we should have to go on forever; but however far we went we should never emerge from the subjective. Moreover, we could begin the same game with the predicate too, and not merely with the predicate *actual*; we could do it just as well with, say, *sweet*. We should then start off by saying: If actuality (or sweetness) is asserted of an object, then the real predicate is not the object's ideated actuality (or sweetness), but the Transcendent that is presupposed as the ground of being of this thing that is ideated. But we could not relax there; we should be driven ever further without end. What can we learn from this? That psychological logic is on the wrong track entirely if it conceives subject and predicate of a judgment as ideas in the psychological sense, that psychological considerations have no more place in logic than they do in astronomy or geology. If we want to emerge from the subjective at all, we must conceive of knowledge as an activity that does not create what is known but grasps what is already there. The picture of grasping is very well suited to elucidate the matter. If I grasp a pencil, many different events take place in my body: nerves are stimulated, changes occur in the tension and pressure of muscles, tendons, and bones, the circulation of the blood is altered. But the totality of these events neither is the pencil nor creates the pencil; the pencil exists independently of them. And it is essential for grasping that something be there which is grasped; the internal changes alone are not the grasping. In the same way, that which we grasp with the mind also exists independently of this activity, independently of the ideas and their alterations that are a part of this grasping or accompany it; and it is neither identical with the totality of these events nor created by it as a part of our own mental life.

Now let us see how for the psychological logicians, more delicate distinctions within the subject matter are blotted out. For the case of characteristic mark and property this has already been mentioned; a related case is the distinction between object and concept, which I stress, and also that between concepts of first and second level. Naturally these distinctions are indiscernible to psychological logicians; for them everything is just idea. With this goes their wrong conception of those judgments that in everyday language we express by using "there is". This existence Herr Erdmann jumbles up with actuality (Vol. I, p. 311), which, as we saw, also is not clearly distinguished from objectivity. Of what thing are we really asserting that it is actual if we say that there are square roots of four? Is it 2 or –2? But neither the one nor the other is named here in any way at all. And if I wished to say that the number 2 acts or is active or actual, this would be false and wholly different from what I mean by the sentence, "There are square roots of four." The confusion before us is just about the grossest possible; for it is not between concepts of the same level, but rather between a concept of first level and a concept of second level. This is characteristic of the obtuseness of psychological logic. When we have gained a less obstructed viewpoint we may be astonished that such a blunder could be committed by a professional logician, but of course before we can gauge the magnitude of the blunder we must ourselves have grasped the distinction between first- and second-level concepts, and psychological logic will be quite incapable of that. The chief impediment is that its exponents take such fantastic pride in psychological profundity, which is after all nothing but psychological falsification of logic. And that is how our thick logic books come into being; they are bloated with unhealthy psychological fat that conceals all more delicate forms. Thus a fruitful collaboration between mathematicians and logicians is made impossible. While the mathematician defines objects, concepts, and relations, the psychological logician is spying upon the origin and evolution of ideas, and to him at bottom the mathematician's defining can only appear foolish because it does not reproduce the essence of ideation. He looks into his psychological peep-show and tells the mathematician: "I see nothing at all of what you are defining." And the mathematician can only reply: "No wonder, for it is not where you are looking for it."

This may be enough to place my logical standpoint in a clearer light by the contrast. The distance between my view and the psychological logicians' seems to me so enormous that there is no prospect of my book's having any effect on them at present. It seems to me as if the tree that I have planted would have to lift a colossal weight of stone in order to gain space and light. And yet I should not like to abandon entirely the hope that my book might later help to overthrow psychological logic. To that end there surely will be some notice of the book by the mathematicians, notice which will compel psychological logic to come to terms with it. And I believe that I may expect some support from mathematicians; they have at bottom a common cause with me against the psychological logicians. I believe that as soon as the latter so much as condescend to occupy themselves seriously with my book, if only to refute it, then I have won. For the whole of the second part [the Proofs of the Basic Laws of Number], is really a test of my logical convictions. It is *prima facie* improbable that such a structure could be erected on a base that was uncertain or defective. Anyone who holds other convictions has only to try to erect a similar structure upon them, and I think he will perceive that it does not work, or at least does not work so well. As a refutation in this I can only recognize someone's actually demonstrating either that a better, more durable edifice can be erected upon other fundamental convictions, or else that my principles lead to manifestly false conclusions. But no one will be able to do that. May my book, then, even if belatedly, contribute to a renewal of logic.

Jena, July, 1893

G. Frege

EXPOSITION OF
THE BEGRIFFSSCHRIFT

EXPOSITION OF THE BEGRIFFSSCHRIFT

1 **§0. Our task. Demands on the conduct of proof. Dedekind's system. Schröder's class.**

In my *Grundlagen der Arithmetik*,[1] I sought to make it plausible that arithmetic is a branch of logic and need not borrow any ground of proof whatever from either experience or intuition. In the present book this shall now be confirmed, by the derivation of the simplest laws of Numbers by logical means alone. But for this to be convincing, considerably higher demands must be placed on the conduct of proof than is customary in arithmetic.[2] A few methods of inference must be marked out in advance, and no step may be taken that is not in accordance with one of these. Thus in passing on to a new judgment one must not be satisfied, as the mathematicians have nearly always been hitherto, with the transition's being evidently correct; rather one must split it into the logically simple steps of which it is composed—and of which there are frequently not a few. In this way no presupposition can pass unnoticed; every axiom required must be uncovered. It is indeed precisely the presuppositions made tacitly and without clear awareness that obstruct our insight into the epistemological nature of a law.

For an undertaking of this kind to succeed, it is of course necessary that we grasp precisely the concepts required. This applies particularly to what the mathematicians would like to designate by the word "set". Dedekind[3] uses the word "system" with very much the same purpose. But despite the explanations in my *Grundlagen* four years earlier, a clear insight into the essence of the matter is not to be found in Dedekind, although he occasionally comes near the mark, as here (p. 2): "Such a system *S* . . . is completely determined if for every thing it is

---

[1] Breslau, 1884.
[2] Cf. my *Grundlagen*, §90.
[3] *Was sind und was sollen die Zahlen?* Braunschweig, 1888.

determined whether it is an element of S or not. Hence a system S is the same as a system T (in symbols, $S = T$) if every element of S is also an element of T and every element [of] T is also an element of S." But other passages wander off again, for example the following (pp. 1-2): "It very frequently occurs that different things $a, b, c, \ldots$, regarded for some reason from a common point of view, are put together in the mind; and we say then that they form a *system S.*" Here a presentiment of the truth is indeed contained in the 'common point of view'; but this 'regarding', this 'putting together in the mind', is not an objective characteristic. I ask, in whose mind? If they are put together in one mind but not in another, do they form a system then? What is supposed to be put together in my mind, no doubt must be in my mind: then do the things outside myself not form systems? Is a system a subjective figure in the individual soul? In that case is the constellation Orion a system? And what are its elements? The stars, or the molecules, or the atoms? The following passage is worthy of note (p. 2): "For uniformity of expression it is advantageous to admit also the special case in which a system S consists of a *single* (one and only one) element a, i.e., in which the thing a is an element of S but every thing different from a is not an element of S." Subsequently (p. 3) this is so understood that every element s of a system S can itself be regarded as a system. Since in this case element and system coincide, it is here particularly clear that according to Dedekind it is the elements that really make up the 'system'. E. Schröder in his *Vorlesungen über die Algebra der Logik*[4] progresses a step beyond Dedekind in calling attention to the connection of his systems with concepts—which Dedekind seems to have overlooked. In fact what Dedekind really means when he calls a system part of a system (p. 2) is the subordination of a concept under a concept or an object's falling under a concept: cases that he distinguishes no better than Schröder, owing to an error of conception shared by them both; for Schröder too at bottom regards the elements as what constitute his *class*. With him an empty class may really no more occur than may an empty system with Dedekind; yet the need of it that arises from the nature of the situation makes itself felt, in different ways, with both

------

[4]Leipzig, 1890, p. 253

authors. Dedekind continues the above passage: "On the other hand, for certain reasons we will here wholly exclude the empty system, which contains no element, although for other investigations it can prove convenient to invent such a system." So according to this, such an invention is allowed; only 'for certain reasons' it is waived. Schröder ventures to invent an empty class. Thus as it seems, both are in agreement with many mathematicians in the view that we may invent anything we please that is not there—and even anything that is unthinkable; for if the elements constitute the system, then where the elements are abolished the system goes with them. As to where the limits of this inventive caprice may lie, or whether there are any limits at all, there is to be found little clarity or agreement; yet the correctness of a proof may depend upon it. I believe this question to have been settled, for all reasonable persons, in my *Grundlagen der Arithmetik* (§92 ff.) and in my lecture "Über formale Theorien der Arithmetik."[5] Schröder does 'invent' his 'Null', and thereby entangles himself in great difficulties.[6] Accordingly, while a clear insight is lacking in Schröder as in Dedekind, the true situation nevertheless makes itself felt whereever a system is to be specified. Dedekind then cites properties that a thing must have in order to belong to the system; i.e., he defines a concept by means of its characteristic marks.[7] Now if it is the characteristic marks that make up the concept, and not the objects falling under it, then there are no difficulties or objections against an empty concept. Of course then an object can never be at the same time a concept; and a concept under which falls only one object must not be confused with it. In this way, then, it will finally be acknowledged that a statement of number contains an assertion about a concept.[8] I have reduced Number to the relation of equinumeracy, and reduced the latter to many-one correspondence. Much the same holds for the word "correspondence" as for the word "set"; both are today

---

[5] *Sitzungsberichte der Jenaischen Gesellschaft für Medicin und Naturwissenschaft, Jahrgang 1885,* session of 17th July.

[6] Cf. E. G. Husserl in the *Göttinger gelehrte Anzeigen,* 1891, no. 7, p. 272, where, however, the problems are not solved.

[7] On *concept, object, property, characteristic mark,* cf. my *Grundlagen,* §§38, 47, 53, and my essay "Über Begriff und Gegenstand", in the *Vierteljahrsschrift für wissenschaftliche Philosophie,* Vol. XVI, no. 2 [1892].

[8] §46 of my *Grundlagen.*

used frequently in mathematics, and for the most part there is lacking any deeper insight into what they are really intended to mean. If I am right in thinking that arithmetic is a branch of pure logic, then a purely logical expression must be selected for "correspondence". I choose "relation" for this purpose. Concept and relation are the foundation-stones upon which I erect my structure.

But even when the concepts have been grasped precisely, it would be difficult—in fact, almost impossible—to satisfy without special aid the demands we must here place on the conduct of proof. Such an aid is my Begriffsschrift, and my first task will be to expound it. The following observation may be made before we proceed. It will not always be possible to give a 4 regular definition of everything, precisely because our endeavor must be to trace our way back to what is logically simple, which as such is not properly definable. I must then be satisfied with indicating what I intend by means of hints. Above all I must strive to be understood, and on this account I shall try to unfold the subject gradually and not attempt full generality or a final expression at the very outset. The reader may be surprised at the frequent use made of quotation marks; by their use I distinguish between the cases in which I am speaking of the sign itself, and those in which I am speaking of its denotation. Pedantic as this may appear, I nevertheless hold it to be necessary. It is remarkable how an inaccurate manner of speaking or writing, perhaps originally employed for convenience or brevity but with full consciousness of its inaccuracy, can end in a confusion of thought when once that consciousness has disappeared. But people have succeeded in mistaking numerals for numbers, the name for what is named, the mere auxiliary devices of arithmetic for its real subject matter. Such experiences teach us how necessary it is to place the highest demands on the accuracy of a manner of speaking and writing. And I have taken pains to do justice to these demands, at all events wherever it seemed to me to be of importance.

1. PRIMITIVE SIGNS

i. INTRODUCTION: FUNCTION, CONCEPT, RELATION[9]

§1. The function is unsaturated.

If we are asked to state the original meaning of the word "function" as used in mathematics, it is easy to fall into calling function of x an expression, formed from "x" and particular numbers by use of the notation for sum, product, power, difference, and so on. This is incorrect, because a function is here represented as an *expression*, as a concatenation of signs, not as what is designated thereby. Hence one will attempt to say, in place of "expression", rather "denotation of an expression". But now, there occurs in the expression the letter "x", which does not denote a number as the sign "2" does, for example, but only indeterminately indicates one. For different numerals that we put in the place of "x" we obtain in general different denotations. For example, if for "x" in the expression

$$\text{``}(2 + 3x^2)x\text{''}$$

we substitute the numerals "0", "1", "2", "3" in order, then we obtain as corresponding denotations the numbers $0, 5, 28, 87$. None of these denotations can claim to be our function. The essence of the function manifests itself rather in the connection it establishes between the numbers whose signs we put for "x" and the numbers that then appear as denotations of our expression—a connection intuitively represented in the course of the

---

[9] Cf. my lecture *Über Function und Begriff* (Jena, 1891) and my essay "Über Begriff und Gegenstand", in the *Vierteljahrsschrift für wissenschaftliche Philosophie*, Vol. XVI, no. 2 (1892). My *Begriffsschrift* (Halle, 1879) no longer fully corresponds to my present standpoint, and hence should be used only with caution to elucidate that set forth here.

curve whose equation in rectangular coördinates is
$$"y = (2 + 3x^2)x".$$
Accordingly the essence of the *function* lies in that part of the expression which is there over and above the "x". The expression for a *function* is *in need of completion, unsaturated*. The letter "x" serves only to hold places open for a numeral that is to complete the expression, and in this way renders recognizable the particular type of need for completion that constitutes the specific nature of the function designated above. Hereafter, the letter "ξ" will be used for this purpose instead of "x".[10] This holding-open is to be understood as follows: all places at which "ξ" stands must be filled always by the same sign, never by different ones. I call these places *argument-places*, and that whose sign (name) occupies these places in a given case, I call the *argument* of the function for this case. The function is completed by the argument; what it becomes on completion I call the *value* of the function for the argument. Thus we obtain a name of the value of a function for an argument, if we fill the argument-places in the name of the function with the name of the argument. In this way, for example, "$(2 + 3 \cdot 1^2) \cdot 1$" is a name of the number 5, composed of the function-name "$(2 + 3\xi^2)\xi$" and "1". Thus the argument is not to be counted a part of the *function,* but serves to complete the function, which in itself is *unsaturated*. In the sequel, where use is made of an expression like "the function $\Phi(\xi)$", it is always to be observed that "ξ" contributes to the designation of the function only so far as it renders recognizable the argument-places, but not in such a way that the essence of the function is altered if some sign is substituted for "ξ".

§2. Truth-values. Denotation and sense. Thought. Object.

To the fundamental arithmetical operations mathematicians have added, as constituting functions, the process of proceeding to a limit in its various forms, as infinite series, differential quotients, and integrals; and finally have understood the word "function" so widely that in some cases the connection between argument and value of the function can no longer be designated

[10] However, nothing is here stipulated for the Begriffsschrift. Rather, the "ξ" will not occur at all in the developments of the Begriffsschrift itself; I shall use it only in the exposition of it, and in elucidations.

by the signs of mathematical analysis, but only by words. Another extension has been to admit complex numbers as arguments and consequently as values of functions. In both directions I have gone still farther. That is, while on the one hand the signs of analysis have not hitherto always been sufficient, on the other hand not all of them have been employed in forming function-names, in that "$\xi^2 = 4$" and "$\xi > 2$", for example, were not allowed to count as names of functions—as I allow them to do. But this is also to say that the domain of the values of functions cannot remain restricted to numbers; for if I take as arguments of the function $\xi^2 = 4$ the numbers 0, 1, 2, 3 in order, I do not obtain numbers [as values]. The expressions

$$\text{``}0^2 = 4\text{''}, \text{``}1^2 = 4\text{''}, \text{``}2^2 = 4\text{''}, \text{``}3^2 = 4\text{''}$$

are expressions some of true, some of false thoughts. I put this as follows: the value of the function $\xi^2 = 4$ is either the *truth-value* of what is true or that of what is false. [11]   It can be seen from this that I do not mean to assert anything if I merely write down an equation, but that I merely *designate* a truth-value, just as I do not assert anything if I merely write down "2^2", but merely *designate* a number. I say: the *names* "$2^2 = 4$" and "$3 > 2$" *denote* the same truth-value, which I call for short *the True*. Likewise, for me "$3^2 = 4$" and "$1 > 2$" *denote* the same truth-value, which I call for short *the False*, precisely as the name "2^2" *denotes* the number four. Accordingly I call the number four the *denotation* of "4" and of "2^2", and I call the True the denotation of "$3 > 2$". However, I distinguish from the *denotation* of a name its *sense*. "2^2" and "$2 + 2$" do not have the same *sense*, nor do "$2^2 = 4$" and "$2 + 2 = 4$" have the same *sense*. The sense of a name of a truth-value I call a *thought*. I further say a name *expresses* its sense and *denotes* its denotation. I *designate* with the name that which it denotes.

Thus the function $\xi^2 = 4$ can have only two values, namely the True for the arguments 2 and -2, and the False for all other arguments.

The domain of what is admitted as argument must also be extended to objects in general. *Objects* stand opposed to functions. Accordingly I count as *objects* everything that is not a

[11] I have justified this more thoroughly in my essay "Über Sinn und Bedeutung" in the *Zeitschrift für Philosophie und philosophische Kritik*, 100 (1892).

function, for example, numbers, truth-values, and the courses-of-values to be introduced below. The names of objects—the *proper names*—therefore carry no argument-places; they are saturated, like the objects themselves.

§3. Course-of-values of a function. Concept. Extension of a concept.

I use the words
> "the function $\Phi(\xi)$ has the same *course-of-values* as the function $\Psi(\xi)$"

generally to denote the same as the words
> "the functions $\Phi(\xi)$ and $\Psi(\xi)$ have always the same value for the same argument".

We have this circumstance with the functions $\xi^2 = 4$ and $3\xi^2 = 12$, at least if numbers are taken as arguments. However, we can imagine the signs for squaring and multiplication to be so defined that the function

$$(\xi^2 = 4) = (3\xi^2 = 12)$$

has the True as value for every argument whatever. At this point we may also use an expression from logic: "the concept *square root of 4* has the same extension as the concept *something whose square trebled is 12*". With such functions, whose value is always a truth-value, one may accordingly say, instead of "course-of-values of the function", rather "extension of the concept"; and it seems appropriate to call directly a *concept* a function whose value is always a truth-value.

§4. Functions of two arguments.

Hitherto I have spoken only of functions of a single argument; but we can easily pass on to *functions of two arguments*. These are *doubly in need of completion*, in the sense that a function of one argument is obtained once a completion by means of one argument has been effected. Only by means of yet another completion do we attain an object, and this is then called the *value* of the function for the two arguments. Just as the letter "ξ" served us with functions of one argument, so here we make use of the letters "ξ" and "ζ" to indicate the twofold unsaturatedness of functions of two arguments, as in

$$"(\xi + \zeta)^2 + \zeta".$$

By substituting (for example) "1" for "ζ", we saturate the function in such a way that in $(\xi + 1)^2 + 1$ we still have a function, but of one argument. This way of using the letters "ξ" and "ζ" must always be kept in mind if an expression occurs like "the function $\Phi(\xi,\zeta)$" (cf. n. 10, above). I call the places at which "ξ" stands *ξ-argument-places*, and those at which "ζ" stands *ζ-argument-places*. I say that the ξ-argument-places are *related* to one another, and likewise for the ζ-argument-places; while I call a ξ-argument-place not *related* to a ζ-argument-place.

The functions of two arguments $\xi = \zeta$ and $\xi > \zeta$ always have a truth-value as value (at least if the signs "=" and ">" are appropriately defined). Such functions it will be appropriate to call *relations*. In the first relation, for example, 1 stands to 1, and in general every object to itself; in the second, for example, 2 stands to 1. We say that the object Γ *stands to* the object Δ *in the relation* $\Psi(\xi,\zeta)$ if $\Psi(\Gamma,\Delta)$ is the True. Likewise we say that the object Δ *falls under* the concept $\Phi(\xi)$ if $\Phi(\Delta)$ is the True. Of course it is presupposed in this that the functions $\Phi(\xi)$ and $\Psi(\xi,\zeta)$ always have as value a truth-value.[12]

ii. SIGNS FOR FUNCTIONS

§5. Judgment and thought. Judgment-stroke and horizontal.

We have already said that in a mere equation there is as yet no assertion; "$2 + 3 = 5$" only designates a truth-value, without its being said which of the two it is. Again, if I wrote
$$\text{``}(2 + 3 = 5) = (2 = 2)\text{''}$$
and presupposed that we knew $2 = 2$ to be the True, I still should not have asserted thereby that the sum of 2 and 3 is 5; rather I should only have designated the truth-value of "*2 + 3 = 5*"'s *denoting the same as* "*2 = 2*". We therefore require another special sign to be able to assert something as true. For this

---

[12] There is a difficulty here which can easily obscure the true state of affairs and hence arouse suspicion as to the correctness of my view. If we compare the expression "the truth-value of Δ's *falling under the concept* $\Phi(\xi)$" with "$\Phi(\Delta)$", we see that what really corresponds to the expression "$\Phi(\ )$" is

"the truth-value of ( )'s *falling under the concept* $\Phi(\xi)$",

and not

"the concept $\Phi(\xi)$".

These last words therefore do not really designate a concept (in our sense), even though by their linguistic form it appears as if they do. As to the awkward position in which language here finds itself, cf. my essay "Über Begriff und Gegenstand".

purpose I let the sign " $\vdash$ " precede the name of the truth-value, so that for example in

$$``\vdash 2^2 = 4", [13]$$

it is asserted that the square of 2 is 4. I distinguish the *judgment* from the *thought* in this way: by a *judgment* I understand the acknowledgement of the truth of a *thought*. The presentation in Begriffsschrift of a judgment by use of the sign " $\vdash$ " I call a *proposition of Begriffsschrift* or briefly a *proposition*. I regard this " $\vdash$ " as composed of the vertical line, which I call the *judgment-stroke,* and the horizontal line, which I will now simply call the *horizontal.*[14] The horizontal will mostly occur fused with other signs, as here with the judgment-stroke, and thereby will be protected against confusion with the *minus sign.* Where it does occur apart, for purposes of distinction it must be made somewhat longer than the minus sign. I regard it as a function-name, as follows:

$$\text{———}\Delta$$

is the True if Δ is the True; on the other hand it is the False if Δ is not the True.[15] Accordingly,

$$\text{———}\xi$$

is a function whose value is always a truth-value—or by our stipulation, a concept. Under this concept there falls the True and only the True. Thus,

$$``\text{———}2^2 = 4"$$

10

---

[13] I frequently make use here, in a provisional way, of the notations for the sum, product, power, although these signs have here not yet been defined, to enable me to form examples more easily and to facilitate understanding by means of hints. But we must keep it in mind that nothing is made to rest on the denotations of these notations.

[14] I used to call it the *content-stroke,* when I still combined under the expression "possible content of judgment" what I have now learned to distinguish as truth-value and thought. Cf. my essay "Über Sinn und Bedeutung."

[15] Obviously the sign "Δ" may not be denotationless, but must denote an object. Denotationless names must not occur in the Begriffsschrift. The stipulation above is made in such a way that "———Δ" denotes something under all circumstances so long merely as "Δ" denotes something. Otherwise ———ξ would not be a concept having sharp boundaries, thus in our sense not a concept at all. I here use *capital Greek letters* as if they were names denoting something, although I do not specify their denotation. In the developments of the Begriffsschrift itself they will occur no more than will "ξ" and "ζ".

denotes the same thing as "$2^2 = 4$", namely the True. In order to dispense with brackets I specify that everything standing to the right of the horizontal is to be regarded as a whole that occupies the argument-place of the function-name "——ξ", except as *brackets* prohibit this.

$$\text{``}\underline{}2^2 = 5\text{''}$$

denotes the False, thus the same thing as does "$2^2 = 5$"; as against this,

$$\text{``}\underline{}2\text{''}$$

denotes the False, thus something different from the number 2. If Δ is a truth-value, then ——Δ is the same truth-value, and consequently

$$\Delta = (\underline{}\Delta)$$

is the True. But this is the False if Δ is not a truth-value. We can therefore say that

$$\Delta = (\underline{}\Delta)$$

is the truth-value of Δ's *being a truth-value*.

Accordingly the function ——$\Phi(\xi)$ is a concept and the function ——$\Psi(\xi,\zeta)$ is a relation, regardless of whether $\Phi(\xi)$ is a concept or $\Psi(\xi,\zeta)$ a relation.

Of the two signs of which "⊢" is composed, only the judgment-stroke contains the act of assertion.

§6. Negation-stroke. Amalgamation of horizontals.

We need no special sign to declare a truth-value to be the False, so long as we possess a sign by which either truth-value is changed into the other; it is also indispensable on other grounds. I now stipulate:

The value of the function

$$\neg\xi$$

shall be the False for every argument for which the value of the function

$$\underline{}\xi$$

is the True; and shall be the True for all other arguments.

Accordingly we possess in

$$\neg\xi$$

a function whose value is always a truth-value; it is a concept, under which falls every object with the sole exception of the True. From this it follows that "$\neg\Delta$" always denotes the same thing as "$\neg(\underline{}\Delta)$", and as "$\underline{}\neg\Delta$", and as "$\underline{}\neg(\underline{}\Delta)$". Hence we regard "$\neg$" as composed of the small vertical stroke, the *negation-stroke*, and the two portions of the horizontal stroke, each of which may be regarded as *horizontals* in our sense. The t r a n s i t i o n from "⊤(——Δ)" or "——⊤Δ" to "—⊤Δ", as well as that from "————Δ" to "——Δ", I call *amalgamation* of horizontals.

By our stipulation ⊤2^2 = 5 is the True; thus:

$$\vdash_{\!\top}2^2 = 5,$$

in words: $2^2 = 5$ is not the True; or: the square of 2 is not 5. So also: $\vdash_{\!\top}2$.

§7. The identity-sign.

We have been using the identity-sign as we went along, to form examples; but it is necessary to stipulate something more precise regarding it.

$$\text{``}\Gamma = \Delta\text{''}$$

shall denote the True if Γ is the same as Δ; in all other cases it shall denote the False.

In order to dispense with brackets I specify that everything standing to the left of the identity-sign as far as the nearest horizontal, as a whole denotes the ξ-argument of the function $\xi = \zeta$, except as *brackets* prohibit this; and that everything standing to the right of the identity-sign as far as the nearest identity-sign, as a whole denotes the ζ-argument of that function, except as *brackets* prohibit this (cf. p. 39, above).

§8. Generality. Gothic letters. Their scope. Amalgamation of horizontals.

We considered in §3 the case in which an equation such as

$$\text{``}\Phi(x) = \Psi(x)\text{''}$$

always yields a name of the True, whatever proper name we may substitute for "x", provided only that this name actually denotes an object. We then have the generality of an identity, whereas in "$2^2 = 4$" we have only an identity. This difference manifests itself in the fact that in the former case we have a letter "x" that i n d i c a t e s only indeterminately, whereas in "$2^2 = 4$" every sign has a determinate denotation. To obtain an expression for the generality, we might think of a definition of this sort:

> 'By "$\Phi(x)$" is to be understood the True, if the value of the function $\Phi(\xi)$ is the True for every argument; otherwise it denotes the False.'

40

It would be assumed here, as in all our considerations of this sort, that "$\Phi(\xi)$" always acquires a denotation if in it we replace "ξ" by a name that denotes an object. Otherwise I should not call $\Phi(\xi)$ a *function*. Accordingly then,

$$\text{``} x \cdot (x - 1) = x^2 - x \text{''}$$

would denote the True, at least if the notations for multiplication, subtraction and squaring were so defined also for objects that are not numbers that the equation did hold universally. On the other hand "$x \cdot (x - 1) = x^2$" would denote the False, because we obtain the False as denotation if we substitute "1" for "x", although we obtain the True if we substitute "0". But by this stipulation the scope of the generality would not be well enough demarcated. A doubt could arise; e.g., whether

$$\text{``} {\,}_{\top} 2 + 3x = 5x \text{''}$$

was to be taken as the negation of a generality or as the generality of a negation; or, more precisely, whether it was supposed to denote the truth-value of

> *the value of the function $2 + 3\xi = 5\xi$'s not being the True for every argument,*

or the truth-value of

> *the value of the function $_{\top} 2 + 3\xi = 5\xi$'s being the True for every argument.*

In the first case, "$_{\top} 2 + 3x = 5x$" would denote the True; in the second, the False. But the negation of the generality must be expressible as well as the generality of the negation. I express the latter thus:

$$\text{``} {\overset{a}{\smile}}_{\top} 2 + 3a = 5a \text{''};$$

and the negation of the generality thus:

$$\text{``} {}_{\top} {\overset{a}{\smile}} 2 + 3a = 5a \text{''};$$

and the generality itself thus:

$$\text{``} {\overset{a}{\smile}} 2 + 3a = 5a \text{''}.$$

This last denotes the True if for every argument the value of the function $2 + 3\xi = 5\xi$ is the True. Since this is not the case, then

$$\overset{a}{\smile} 2 + 3a = 5a$$

is the False, hence

$$_{\top} \overset{a}{\smile} 2 + 3a = 5a$$

is the True.

$$\overset{a}{\smile}_{\top} 2 + 3a = 5a$$

is the False, because the value of the function $_{\top} 2 + 3\xi = 5\xi$

41

is not the True for every argument; for it is the False for the argument 1. Consequently

$$\text{—}\underset{a}{\curlywedge}\text{—}\ 2 + 3a = 5a$$

is the True, and

$$\text{``}\ \vdash\underset{a}{\curlywedge}\text{—}\ 2 + 3a = 5a\text{''}$$

asserts: *there is* at least one solution of the equation
$$\text{``}2 + 3x = 5x\text{''}.$$

In the same way,

$$\vdash\underset{a}{\curlywedge}\text{—}\ a^2 = 1;$$

in words: *there is* at least one square root of 1. We see from this how *"there is"* is to be rendered in the Begriffsschrift.

If we now set up the definition as follows:

> "$\underset{a}{\curlywedge}\Phi(a)$" is to denote the True if for every argument the value of the function $\Phi(\xi)$ is the True, and otherwise is to denote the False,

a supplementation is required: namely, a more exact statement as to what this function $\Phi(\xi)$ is in every case. We will call it the *corresponding* function. For uncertainties can arise; $\Delta = \Delta$ is as much the value of the function $\Delta = \xi$ as it is of the function $\xi = \xi$, in both cases for the argument Δ. Thus someone starting from $\underset{a}{\curlywedge}a = a$ might take either $\xi = a$, or $a = \xi$, or $\xi = \xi$ to be the corresponding function. However, by our use of Gothic letters we should have in the first two cases no *function* at all, because "$\xi = a$" and "$a = \xi$" never denote anything, whatever one may substitute for the "ξ": the Gothic letter "a" may not occur without "$\underset{a}{\curlywedge}$" prefixed, save in "$\underset{a}{\curlywedge}$" itself. Therefore only "$\xi = \xi$" may here be considered our corresponding function. The case is less simple with an expression like

$$\text{``}\underset{a}{\curlywedge}[(a + a = 2a) = (\underset{a}{\curlywedge}a = a)]\text{''}.$$

If we went ahead blindly, we could think we had the corresponding function in

$$\text{``}(\xi + \xi = 2\xi) = (\underset{\xi}{\curlywedge}\xi = \xi)\text{''}.$$

I will now say, "a" stands in "$\underset{a}{\curlywedge}$" over the *concavity*. The place over the concavity is never an *argument-place*; therefore at least the "a" standing over the second concavity is to be preserved. But since the "$\underset{a}{\curlywedge}$" must always be followed by a combination of signs that includes "a", it follows that "a" must remain intact in at least one of the two places in "$a = a$". Accordingly we might incline toward these functions as corresponding:

13

42

$$(\xi + \xi = 2\xi) = (\underset{a}{\smile}\, \xi = a),$$
$$(\xi + \xi = 2\xi) = (\underset{a}{\smile}\, a = \xi),$$
$$(\xi + \xi = 2\xi) = (\underset{a}{\smile}\, a = a);$$

but against the first two notions is the fact that the denotation of the "$\underset{a}{\smile}\, a = a$" occurring in

$$\text{``}\underset{a}{\smile}[(a + a = 2a) = (\underset{a}{\smile}\, a = a)]\text{''}$$

is already established, and may not be called back into question.

Let us call that which follows a concavity containing a *Gothic letter* and which together with this concavity forms the name of the truth-value of *the value of the corresponding function's being the True for every argument,* the *scope* of the Gothic letter standing over the concavity. The *corresponding* function is now determined by the following rule:

1. All places at which there occurs a Gothic letter within its scope, yet not within an enclosed scope of the same letter, and not over a concavity, are related argument-places, namely those of the corresponding function.

But if we want to designate the truth-value of *the function*

$$(\xi + \xi = 2\xi) = (\underset{a}{\smile}\, \xi = a)\text{'s}$$

having the True as value for every argument, then we shall choose a different Gothic letter:

$$\underset{e}{\smile}(e + e = 2e) = (\underset{a}{\smile}\, e = a).$$

14 I comprise this in the following rule:

2. If in the name of a function Gothic letters already occur, within whose scope lie argument-places of this function, then to form the corresponding expression of generality a Gothic letter different from these must be chosen.

According to our stipulations, one Gothic letter is in general as good as another, with the restriction however that distinctness among these letters can be essential. For certain Gothic letters we shall later lay down a somewhat different type of use. "$\underset{a}{\smile}\Phi(a)$" denotes the same thing as "$\underset{a}{\smile}(\underline{\quad}\Phi(a))$" and "$\underline{\quad}(\underset{a}{\smile}\Phi(a))$". Hence I regard the horizontal strokes to the right and left of the concavity in "$\underset{a}{\smile}$" as *horizontals* in our special sense of the word, so that by *amalgamation* of horizontals we can pass over immediately from the forms "$\underline{\quad}(\underset{a}{\smile}\Phi(a))$" and "$\underset{a}{\smile}(\underline{\quad}\Phi(a))$" to "$\underset{a}{\smile}\Phi(a)$".

§9. Notation for the course-of-values. Small Greek vowels. Their scope.

If $\underset{a}{\smile}\Phi(a) = \Psi(a)$ is the True, then by our earlier stipulation

($3) we can also say that the function $\Phi(\xi)$ has the same course-of-values as the function $\Psi(\xi)$; i.e., we can transform the generality of an identity into an identity of courses-of-values and vice versa. This possibility must be regarded as a law of logic, a law that is invariably employed, even if tacitly, whenever discourse is carried on about the extensions of concepts. The whole Leibniz-Boole calculus of logic rests upon it. One might perhaps regard this transformation as unimportant or even as dispensable. As against this, I recall the fact that in my *Grundlagen der Arithmetik* I defined a Number as the extension of a concept, and indicated then that negative, irrational, in short all numbers were to be defined as extensions of concepts. We can set down a simple sign for a course-of-values, and in that way for example the name of the Number Nought will be introduced. On the other hand, in

$$\text{``}\overset{a}{\smile}\Phi(a) = \Psi(a)\text{''}$$

we cannot put a simple sign for "$\Phi(a)$", because the letter "a" must always occur in whatever is substituted for "$\Phi(a)$".

The conversion of the generality of an identity into an identity of courses-of-values has to be capable of being carried out in our symbolism. Therefore, e.g., for

$$\text{``}\overset{a}{\smile}a^2 - a = a \cdot (a - 1)\text{''},$$

I write

$$\text{``}\grave{\epsilon}(\epsilon^2 - \epsilon) = \grave{a}(a \cdot (a - 1))\text{''},$$

in which by "$\grave{\epsilon}(\epsilon^2 - \epsilon)$" I understand the course-of-values of the function $\xi^2 - \xi$, and by "$\grave{a}(a \cdot (a - 1))$" the course-of-values of the function $\xi \cdot (\xi - 1)$. Similarly, $\grave{\epsilon}(\epsilon^2 = 4)$ is the course-of-values of the function $\xi^2 = 4$, or, as we can also say, the extension of the concept *square root of 4*.

If I say generally that

"$\grave{\epsilon}\Phi(\epsilon)$" denotes the course-of-values of the function $\Phi(\xi)$, this requires a supplementation like that in $\S 8$, above, in our explanation of "$\overset{a}{\smile}\Phi(a)$"; i.e., the question is which function in each case is to be regarded as the *corresponding* function $\Phi(\xi)$. It is obvious that $\grave{\epsilon}(\epsilon^2 - \epsilon)$ is the course-of-values of the function $\xi^2 - \xi$, and not of $\xi^2 - \epsilon$ or $\epsilon^2 - \xi$, because by our way of using *small Greek vowels* neither "$\xi^2 - \epsilon$" nor "$\epsilon^2 - \xi$" would acquire a denotation for any object whose name was substituted for "ξ", or as we can also put it, because these combinations of signs do not denote any functions but rather, separated from

15

44

the "$\acute\epsilon$", are devoid of denotation. A combination of signs like

$$\text{``}\acute\epsilon\,\Psi(\epsilon,\ \acute\epsilon X(\epsilon))\text{''}$$

must be adjudicated as in §8 with "$\underset{\smile}{\alpha}\Psi(\alpha,\ \underset{\smile}{\alpha}X(\alpha))$". The place under the smooth breathing is no more an *argument-place* than that over the concavity. Let us call what follows a *small Greek vowel* with the smooth breathing, and together with this forms the name of the course-of-values of the *corresponding* function, the *scope* of this Greek vowel. Then we can set up the following rule:

1. All places at which there occurs a small Greek vowel within its scope, yet not within an enclosed scope of the same letter, and not with a smooth breathing, are related argument-places, namely those of the corresponding function.

This is hereby stipulated. Accordingly $\acute\epsilon(\epsilon = \acute\epsilon(\epsilon^2 - \epsilon))$ is the course-of-values of the function $\xi = \acute\epsilon(\epsilon^2 - \epsilon)$, and $\acute\alpha(\alpha = \acute\epsilon(\epsilon = \alpha)$ the course-of-values of the function $\xi = \acute\epsilon(\epsilon = \xi)$. For the formation of a name of a course-of-values the following rule also holds:

2. If in the name of a function small Greek vowels already occur, within whose scope lie argument-places of this function, then to form the name of the course-of-values of this function a Greek vowel different from these must be chosen.

According to our stipulations, one small Greek vowel is in general as good as another, with the restriction however that distinctness among these letters can be essential.

The introduction of a notation for courses-of-values seems to me to be one of the most important supplementations that I have made of my Begriffsschrift since my first publication on this subject. By introducing it we also extend the domain of arguments of any function. For example,

$$\acute\epsilon(\epsilon^2 - \epsilon) = \acute\alpha(\alpha\cdot(\alpha - 1))$$

is the value of the function

$$\xi = \acute\alpha(\alpha\cdot(\alpha - 1))$$

for the argument $\acute\epsilon(\epsilon^2 - \epsilon)$.

§10. The course-of-values of a function more exactly specified.

Although we have laid it down that the combination of signs

$$\text{``}\acute\epsilon\,\Phi(\epsilon) = \acute\alpha\Psi(\alpha)\text{''}$$

has the same denotation as

$$\text{``}\underset{\smile}{\alpha}\Phi(\alpha) = \Psi(\alpha)\text{''},$$

this by no means fixes completely the denotation of a name like "$\acute{\epsilon}\Phi(\epsilon)$". We have only a means of always recognizing a course-of-values if it is designated by a name like "$\acute{\epsilon}\Phi(\epsilon)$", by which it is already recognizable as a course-of-values. But we can neither decide, so far, whether an object is a course-of-values that is not given us as such, and to what function it may correspond, nor decide in general whether a given course-of-values has a given property unless we know that this property is connected with a property of the corresponding function. If we assume that

$$X(\xi)$$

is a function that never takes on the same value for different arguments, then for objects whose names are of the form

$$\text{``}X(\acute{\epsilon}\,\Phi(\epsilon))\text{''}$$

just the same distinguishing mark for recognition holds, as for objects signs for which are of the form "$\acute{\epsilon}\Phi(\epsilon)$". To wit,

$$\text{``}X(\acute{\epsilon}\Phi(\epsilon)) = X(\acute{a}\Psi(a))\text{''}$$

then also has the same denotation as "$\underset{a}{\frown}\Phi(a) = \Psi(a)$". [16] From this it follows that by identifying the denotation of "$\acute{\epsilon}\Phi(\epsilon) = \acute{a}\Psi(a)$" with that of "$\underset{a}{\frown}\Phi(a) = \Psi(a)$", we have by no means fully determined the denotation of a name like "$\acute{\epsilon}\Phi(\epsilon)$"—at least if there does exist such a function $X(\xi)$ whose value for a course-of-values as argument is not always the same as the course-of-values itself. How may this indefiniteness be overcome? By its being determined for every function when it is introduced, what values it takes on for courses-of-values as arguments, just as for all other arguments. Let us do this for the functions considered up to this point. There are the following:

$$\xi = \zeta, \quad \text{——}\ \xi, \quad \text{—}_\top\ \xi.$$

We can leave the last out of account, since it can be considered always to take a truth-value as argument. With this function it makes no difference whether one takes as argument an object, or the value of the function ——ξ for this object as argument. Now we can still reduce the function ——ξ to the function $\xi = \zeta$. That is, by our stipulations the function $\xi = (\xi = \xi)$ has for every argument the same value as the function ——ξ; for the value of the function $\xi = \xi$ is the True for every argument. From this it follows that the value of the function $\xi = (\xi = \xi)$ is the True 17

---

[16] This is not to say that the sense is the same.

only for the True as argument, and that it is the False for all other arguments, exactly as with the function —— ξ. Since in this way everything reduces to consideration of the function $\xi = \zeta$, we ask what value this has if a course-of-values occurs as argument. Since up to now we have introduced only the truth-values and courses-of-values as objects, it can only be a question of whether one of the truth-values can perhaps be a course-of-values. If not, then it is thereby also decided that the value of the function $\xi = \zeta$ is always the False if a truth-value is taken as one of its arguments and a course-of-values as the other. If on the other hand the True is at the same time the course-of-values of some function $\Phi(\xi)$, then it is thereby also decided what the value of the function $\xi = \zeta$ is in all cases in which the True is taken as one of the arguments, and likewise if the False is at the same time the course-of-values of a certain function. Now the question whether one of the truth-values is a course-of-values cannot be decided from the fact that

$$``\acute{\epsilon}\Phi(\epsilon) = \acute{a}\Psi(a)"$$

is to have the same denotation as

$$``\underset{a}{\smile}\Phi(a) = \Psi(a)".$$

It is possible to stipulate generally that

$$``\overline{\eta}\Phi(\eta) = \overline{a}\Psi(a)"$$

shall denote the same thing as

$$``\underset{a}{\smile}\Phi(a) = \Psi(a)"$$

without the identity of $\acute{\epsilon}\Phi(\epsilon)$ and $\overline{\eta}\Phi(\eta)$ being derivable from this. We should then have a class of objects with names of the form $``\overline{\eta}\Phi(\eta)"$, and for whose differentiation and recognition the same distinguishing mark held good as for courses-of-values. We could now determine the function $X(\xi)$ by saying that its value shall be the True for $\overline{\eta}\Lambda(\eta)$ as argument, and shall be $\overline{\eta}\Lambda(\eta)$ for the True as argument; further the value of the function $X(\xi)$ shall be the False for the argument $\overline{\eta}M(\eta)$, and shall be $\overline{\eta}M(\eta)$ for the False as argument; for every other argument the value of the function $X(\xi)$ is to coincide with the argument itself. If now the functions $\Lambda(\xi)$ and $M(\xi)$ do not always have the same value for the same argument, then our function $X(\xi)$ never has the same value for different arguments, hence

$$``X(\overline{\eta}\Phi(\eta)) = X(\overline{a}\Psi(a))"$$

also always has the same denotation as

$$``\underset{a}{\smile}\Phi(a) = \Psi(a)".$$

The objects whose names were of the form "$X(\overline{\eta}\Phi(\eta))$" would then be recognized by the same means as the courses-of-values, and $X(\overline{\eta}\Lambda(\eta))$ would be the True and $X(\overline{\eta}M(\eta))$ the False. Thus without contradicting our setting

$$\text{``}\acute{\epsilon}\,\Phi(\epsilon) = \acute{\epsilon}\,\Psi(\epsilon)\text{''}$$

equal to

$$\text{``}\underset{a}{\frown}\Phi(a) = \Psi(a)\text{''}$$

it is always possible to stipulate that an arbitrary course-of-values is to be the True and another the False. Accordingly let us lay it down that $\acute{\epsilon}(\text{———}\,\epsilon)$ is to be the True and $\acute{\epsilon}(\epsilon = (\underset{a}{\frown}\,a = a))$ is to be the False. $\acute{\epsilon}(\text{———}\,\epsilon)$ is the course-of-values of the function $\text{———}\,\xi$, whose value is the True only if the argument is the True, and whose value for all other arguments is the False. All functions for which this holds, have the same course-of-values, and this is by our stipulation the True. Accordingly $\text{———}\,\acute{\epsilon}\Phi(\epsilon)$ is the True only if the function $\Phi(\xi)$ is a concept under which falls only the True; in all other cases $\text{———}\,\acute{\epsilon}\Phi(\epsilon)$ is the False. Further, $\acute{\epsilon}(\epsilon = (\underset{a}{\frown}\,a = a))$ is the course-of-values of the function $\xi = (\underset{a}{\frown}\,a = a)$, whose value is the True only if the argument is the False, and whose value for all other arguments is the False. All functions for which this holds have the same course-of-values, and this is by our stipulation the False. Thus every concept under which falls the False and only the False, has as its extension the False. [17]

18

<hr/>

[17] A natural suggestion is to generalize our stipulation so that every object is regarded as a course-of-values, viz., as the extension of a concept under which it and it alone falls. A concept under which the object Δ and Δ alone falls is $\Delta = \xi$. Suppose we attempt the stipulation: let $\acute{\epsilon}(\Delta = \epsilon)$ be the same as Δ. Such a stipulation is possible for every object that is given us independent of courses-of-values on the same basis as we have observed with the truth-values. But before it may be generalized, the question arises whether it may not contradict our notation for recognizing courses-of-values if we take for Δ an object that is already given us as a course-of-values. In particular it is intolerable to allow it to hold only for such objects as are not given us as courses-of-values; the way in which an object is given must not be regarded as an immutable property of it, since the same object can be given in a different way. Thus if we substitute "$\acute{a}\Phi(a)$" for "Δ", then we obtain

$$\text{``}\acute{\epsilon}(\acute{a}\Phi(a) = \epsilon) = \acute{a}\Phi(a)\text{''},$$

and this would denote the same as

$$\text{``}\underset{a}{\frown}(\acute{a}\Phi(a) = a) = \Phi(a)\text{''},$$

48

With this we have determined the courses-of-values so far as is here possible. As soon as there is a further question of introducing a function that is not completely reducible to functions known already, we can stipulate what value it is to have for courses-of-values as arguments; and this can then be regarded as much as a further determination of the courses-of-values as of that function.

§ 11. Substitute for the definite article: the function $\backslash\xi$.

In fact, we do require such functions still. If the equating of "$\acute{\epsilon}(\Delta = \epsilon)$" with "$\Delta$" were allowed generally to stand,[18] then we should have a substitute in the form $\acute{\epsilon}\,\Phi(\epsilon)$ for the definite article of ordinary language. That is, assuming $\Phi(\xi)$ to be a concept under which fell the object Δ and only Δ, then $-\!\!\!-^{a}\Phi(a) = (\Delta = a)$ would be the True, and consequently $\acute{\epsilon}\,\Phi(\epsilon) = \acute{\epsilon}(\Delta = \epsilon)$ would also be the True, and by virtue of our equating of "$\acute{\epsilon}(\Delta = \epsilon)$" with "$\Delta$", $\acute{\epsilon}\Phi(\epsilon)$ would be the same as Δ; i.e., in the case in which $\Phi(\xi)$ was a concept under which one and only one object fell, "$\acute{\epsilon}\Phi(\epsilon)$" would designate this object. Now of course this is not possible, because that equation could not be sustained in its general form, but we can serve our purpose by introducing the function

$$\backslash\xi$$

with the stipulation that two cases are to be distinguished:

1. If to the argument there corresponds an object Δ such that the argument is $\acute{\epsilon}(\Delta = \epsilon)$, then let the value of the function $\backslash\xi$ be Δ itself;

---

which however denotes the True only if $\Phi(\xi)$ is a concept under which one and only one object falls, namely $\grave{a}\Phi(a)$. Since this last is not necessary, our stipulation cannot remain intact in its general form.

The identity "$\acute{\epsilon}(\Delta = \epsilon) = \Delta$" with which we have tested this stipulation is a special case of "$\acute{\epsilon}\Omega(\epsilon,\,\Delta) = \Delta$", and one may ask how the function $\Omega(\xi,\,\zeta)$ would have to be constituted so that it might be generally determined that Δ was to be the same as $\acute{\epsilon}\Omega(\epsilon,\,\Delta)$. Then

$$\acute{\epsilon}\,\Omega(\epsilon,\,\grave{a}\Phi(a)) = \grave{a}\Phi(a)$$

must be the True, consequently

$$-\!\!\!-^{a}\,\Omega(a,\,\grave{a}\Phi(a)) = \Phi(a)$$

must be the True as well, whatever function $\Phi(\xi)$ may be. We shall later become acquainted with a function having this property in the function $\xi\cap\zeta$; but we shall define this with the aid of the course-of-values, so that we can make no use of it here.

[18] See n. 17, above.

49

2. if to the argument there does not correspond an object Δ such that the argument is $\acute{\epsilon}(\Delta = \epsilon)$, then let the value of the function be the argument itself.

Accordingly $\backslash\acute{\epsilon}(\Delta = \epsilon) = \Delta$ is the True, and "$\backslash\acute{\epsilon}\Phi(\epsilon)$" denotes the object falling under the concept $\Phi(\xi)$ if $\Phi(\xi)$ is a concept under which falls one and only one object; in all other cases "$\backslash\acute{\epsilon}\Phi(\epsilon)$" denotes the same as "$\acute{\epsilon}\Phi(\epsilon)$". Thus for example, $2 = \backslash\acute{\epsilon}(\epsilon + 3 = 5)$ is the True, because 2 is the one and only object that falls under the concept

what when increased by 3 yields 5

—a proper definition of the plus sign being p r e s u p p o s e d. $\acute{\epsilon}(\epsilon^2 = 1) = \backslash\acute{\epsilon}(\epsilon^2 = 1)$ is the True, because more than one single object falls under the concept *square root of 1*.

$$\acute{\epsilon}(\overline{}\,\epsilon = \epsilon) = \backslash\acute{\epsilon}(\overline{}\,\epsilon = \epsilon)$$

is the True, because no object falls under the concept *not identical with itself*. $\acute{\epsilon}(\epsilon + 3) = \backslash\acute{\epsilon}(\epsilon + 3)$ [is the True], because the function $\xi + 3$ is not a concept.

We have here a substitute for the definite article of ordinary language, which serves to form proper names out of concept-words. For example, we form from the words

"positive square root of 2",

which denote a concept, the proper name

"the positive square root of 2".

Here there is a logical danger. For if we wanted to form from the words "square root of 2" the proper name "the square root of 2" we should commit a logical error, because this proper name, in the absence of further stipulation, would be ambiguous,[19] hence even devoid of denotation. If there were no irrational numbers—as has indeed been maintained—then even the proper name "the positive square root of 2" would be without a denotation, at least by the straightforward sense of the words, without special stipulation. And if we were to give this proper name a denotation expressly, the object denoted would have no connection with the formation of the name, and we should not be entitled to infer that it was a positive square root of 2, while yet we should be only too inclined to conclude just that. This danger about the definite article is here completely circumvented, since "$\backslash\acute{\epsilon}\Phi(\epsilon)$" always has a denotation, whether the function $\Phi(\xi)$ be not a concept, or a concept under which falls

20

---

[19] I am taking for granted here that there exist negative and irrational numbers.

no object or more than one, or a concept under which falls exactly one object.

§12. Condition-stroke. And. Neither-nor. Or. Subcomponents. Main component.

In order to enable us to designate the subordination of a concept under a concept, and other important relations, I introduce the function of two arguments

$$\unicode{x294}{\xi \atop \zeta}$$

by stipulating that its value shall be the False if the True be taken as ζ-argument and any object other than the True be taken as ξ-argument, and that in all other cases the value of the function shall be the True. By these and earlier stipulations the value of this function is specified also for courses-of-values as arguments. It follows that

$$\unicode{x294}{\Gamma \atop \Delta}$$

is the same as

$$-\left(\unicode{x294}{(-\!\!-\Gamma) \atop (-\!\!-\Delta)}\right),$$

hence in

$$``\unicode{x294}{\Gamma \atop \Delta}\text{''}$$

we can regard the horizontal stroke in front of "Δ", as well as the two parts into which the upper horizontal stroke is divided by the vertical, as *horizontals* in our specific sense. We speak here, as earlier, of the *amalgamation of horizontals*. The vertical stroke I call the *condition-stroke*. It may be lengthened as required.

The following propositions hold:

$$``\unicode{x295}{3^2 > 2 \atop 3 > 2}\text{''},\qquad ``\unicode{x295}{2^2 > 2 \atop 2 > 2}\text{''},\qquad ``\unicode{x295}{1^2 > 2 \atop 1 > 2}\text{''}.$$

The function $\unicode{x2aec}{\xi \atop \zeta}$ or $-\unicode{x294}{\xi \atop \zeta}$ has as value always the True if the function $\unicode{x294}{\xi \atop \zeta}$ has as value the False, and conversely. Therefore

21 $\unicode{x2aec}{\Gamma \atop \Delta}$ is the True if and only if Δ is the True and Γ is not the True. Consequently

$$\unicode{x295}{2 > 3 \atop 2 + 3 = 5};$$

in words: 2 is not greater than 3 *and* the sum of 2 and 3 is 5.

$$\vdash_{\sqcap\!\!\sqcup} \begin{array}{l} 3 > 2 \\ 2 + 3 = 5; \end{array}$$

in words: 3 is greater than 2 *and* the sum of 2 and 3 is 5. That is,

$$\top_{\sqcup} \begin{array}{l} 3 > 2 \\ 2 + 3 = 5 \end{array}$$

is the value of the function $\top_{\sqcup} \begin{array}{l} \xi \\ \zeta \end{array}$ for the ξ-argument $\top 3 > 2$ and the ζ-argument $2 + 3 = 5$.

$$\vdash_{\sqcap\!\!\top} \begin{array}{l} 2^3 = 3^2 \\ 1^2 = 2^1; \end{array}$$

in words: *neither* is the third power of 2 the second power of 3, *nor* is the second power of 1 the first power of 2.

In place of the propositions

"$\vdash_{\sqcap\!\top} \begin{array}{l} 3^2 > 3 \\ 3 < 3 \end{array}$" , "$\vdash_{\sqcap\!\top} \begin{array}{l} 2^2 > 3 \\ 2 < 3 \end{array}$" , "$\vdash_{\sqcap\!\top} \begin{array}{l} 1^2 > 3 \\ 1 < 3 \end{array}$" ,

we have the following:

"$\vdash_{\sqcap\!\!\top} \begin{array}{l} 3^2 > 3 \\ 3 < 3 \end{array}$" , "$\vdash_{\sqcap\!\top} \begin{array}{l} 2^2 > 3 \\ 2 < 3 \end{array}$" , "$\vdash_{\sqcap\!\top} \begin{array}{l} 1^2 > 3 \\ 1 < 3 \end{array}$" .

Now since $\top_{\top} \begin{array}{l} 1^2 > 3 \\ 1 < 3 \end{array}$ is the truth-value of *neither the square of 1's*

being greater than 3 nor 1's being smaller than 3, this is negated by our last proposition above; thus it is affirmed that of the following two at least one is true: either that the square of 1 is greater than 3, *or* that 1 is smaller than 3. We see from these examples how the *"and"* of ordinary language (used as a sentence-connective), the *"neither-nor"*, and the *"or"* between sentences, are to be rendered.

In "$\top_{\Delta} \xi$", any proper name may be substituted for "ξ", thus also, for example, the proper name "$\top_{\Lambda} \Theta$". In this way we obtain

$$\text{``} \top_{\sqcup\Delta} \left(\top_{\Lambda} \Theta \right) \text{''} ,$$

in which we may now *amalgamate* the horizontals:

$$\text{``} \top_{\sqcup} \begin{array}{l} \Theta \\ \Lambda \\ \Delta \end{array} \text{''} .$$

This denotes the False if Δ is the True and $\top_{\Lambda} \Theta$ is not the True,   22 i.e., in this case if $\underset{\Lambda}{\top}\!\!-\Theta$ is the False. But this is the case if and only if Λ is the True and Θ is not the True. Accordingly,

$$\top\!\!\begin{array}{l}\llcorner\Theta\\\llcorner\Lambda\\\llcorner\Delta\end{array}$$

is the False if Δ and Λ are the True while Θ is not the True; in all other cases it is the True. From this there follows the interchangeability of Λ and Δ;

$$\top\!\!\begin{array}{l}\llcorner\Theta\\\llcorner\Lambda\\\llcorner\Delta\end{array}$$

is the same truth-value as

$$\top\!\!\begin{array}{l}\llcorner\Theta\\\llcorner\Delta\\\llcorner\Lambda\end{array}.$$

In

$$``\;\top\!\!\begin{array}{l}\llcorner\Theta\\\llcorner\Delta\\\llcorner\Lambda\end{array}``\;,$$

we may call "——Θ" the *main component* and "——Δ" and "——Λ" *subcomponents*; however, we may also regard "$\underset{\Delta}{\top}\!\!-\Theta$" as the *main component* and "——Λ" alone as *subcomponent*. The subcomponents are accordingly *interchangeable*. In the same way we see that

$$\top\!\!\begin{array}{l}\llcorner\Theta\\\llcorner\Lambda\\\llcorner\Delta\\\llcorner\Xi\end{array}$$

is the False if and only if both Λ and Δ and Ξ are the True while Θ is not the True; in all other cases it is the True. Here too we have *interchangeability of the subcomponents* "——Λ", "——Δ" and "——Ξ". This interchangeability must properly be proved for every case that arises, and I have done this in my booklet *Begriffsschrift* for certain cases in such a way that it is easy to treat every case accordingly. So as not to become tied up in excessive complexity, I here wish to assume this interchangeability generally granted, and to make use of it in future without further explicit mention.

is the True if and only if both Λ and Δ and Ξ are the True while Θ is not the True. Accordingly,

$$
\begin{array}{l}
3 < 2 \\
1 < 2 \\
3 > 2 \\
4 > 2 ;
\end{array}
$$

in words: 3 is not smaller than 2 and 1 is smaller than 2 and 3 is greater than 2 and 4 is greater than 2;

$$
\begin{array}{l}
1 < 2 \\
3 > 2 \\
4 > 2 ;
\end{array}
$$

in words: 1 is smaller than 2 and 3 is greater than 2 and 4 is greater than 2. We may imagine it split up as follows:

$$
\text{``} \ \left(\begin{array}{l} 1 < 2 \\ 3 > 2 \end{array} \right) \text{''}
$$
$$
4 > 2 \qquad ;
$$

in which the two negation-strokes between the condition-strokes may be canceled and the horizontals amalgamated. In

$$
\begin{array}{l}
1 < 2 \\
3 > 2 \\
4 > 2
\end{array}
$$

we have the value of the function $\begin{array}{l}\xi\\\zeta\end{array}$ for the ξ-argument $\begin{array}{l}1<2\\3>2\end{array}$ and the ζ-argument $4 > 2$, where $\begin{array}{l}1<2\\3>2\end{array}$ is the value of the same function for the ξ-argument $1 < 2$ and the ζ-argument $3 > 2$.

13. If. All. Every. Subordination. Particular affirmative proposition. Some.

To justify the nomenclature "condition-stroke", let me point out that the names "$\begin{array}{l}3^2 > 2\\3 > 2\end{array}$", "$\begin{array}{l}2^2 > 2\\2 > 2\end{array}$", "$\begin{array}{l}1^2 > 2\\1 > 2\end{array}$", result from "$\begin{array}{l}\xi^2 > 2\\\xi > 2\end{array}$" by "3", "2", "1" being substituted for "ξ".

Let us now employ the sign "$>$" in such a way that "$\Gamma > \Delta$" denotes the True if Γ and Δ are real numbers and Γ is greater than Δ, and that "$\Gamma > \Delta$" denotes the False in all other cases; let us further assume that the notation "Γ^2" is so defined that it always has a denotation if Γ is an object; then the value of the function

$$\left\lvert\!\!\begin{array}{l} \xi^2 > 2 \\ \xi > 2 \end{array}\right.$$

is the True for every argument. Therefore,

$$\left\vert\!\!\!\!\begin{array}{c} a \\ \rule{0pt}{0pt} \end{array}\!\!\!\!\left\lvert\!\!\begin{array}{l} a^2 > 2 \\ a > 2 \end{array}\right. ;$$

in words: *if* something is greater than 2, *then* its square is also greater than 2. Thus too,

$$\left\vert\!\!\!\!\begin{array}{c} a \\ \rule{0pt}{0pt} \end{array}\!\!\!\!\left\lvert\!\!\begin{array}{l} a^4 = 1 \\ a^2 = 1 \end{array}\right. ;$$

in words: *if* the square of something is 1, *then* its fourth power also is 1. But one can also say: *every* square root of 1 is also fourth root of 1; or: *all* square roots of 1 are fourth roots of 1.[20] Here we have the *subordination* of a concept under a concept, a *universal* affirmative proposition. We have called a concept a function of one argument whose value is always a truth-value. Here $\xi^4 = 1$ and $\xi^2 = 1$ are functions of this kind; the latter is the *subordinated*, the former the *superordinated* concept. The concept

$$\left\lvert\!\!\begin{array}{l} \xi^4 = 1 \\ \xi^2 = 1 \end{array}\right.$$

is composed out of these concepts as its characteristic marks; under it falls, for example, the number -1:

$$\left\vert\!\!\!\!\left\lvert\!\!\begin{array}{l} (-1)^4 = 1 \\ (-1)^2 = 1 \end{array}\right. ;$$

in words: -1 is square root of 1 and fourth root of 1. We saw in §8 how the "there is" of natural language is to be rendered; this may be applied so as to express that there is something which is square root of 1 and fourth root of 1: $\left\vert\!\!\!\!\begin{array}{c} a \\ \end{array}\!\!\!\!\left\lvert\!\!\begin{array}{l} a^4 = 1 \\ a^2 = 1 \end{array}\right.$. Plainly two negation-strokes here cancel each other: $\left\vert\!\!\!\!\begin{array}{c} a \\ \end{array}\!\!\!\!\left\lvert\!\!\begin{array}{l} a^4 = 1. \\ a^2 = 1 \end{array}\right.$

Now let us consider this from yet another side. $\begin{array}{c} a \\ \end{array}\!\!\!\!\left\lvert\!\!\begin{array}{l} a^4 = 1 \\ a^2 = 1 \end{array}\right.$ is the truth-value of *if something is square root of 1 then its not being fourth root of 1*; or, as we can also say, of *no square root*

---

[20]It is easy to link this with a related thought, that there exists something which is square root of 1; but we must here hold entirely aloof from this. Likewise we must resist another related thought, that there exists more than one square root of 1.

of 1's being fourth root of 1. This truth-value is the False, and consequently $\vdash\!\!\!\rlap{\raise2pt\hbox{a}}\!\!\!\sqsubset\begin{array}{l} a^4 = 1 \\ a^2 = 1 \end{array}$. Here we have the negation of a universal negative proposition; i.e., we have a *particular* affirmative proposition,[21] for which we can also say: "*some* square roots of 1 are fourth roots of 1", in which, however, the plural form must not be so understood that there has to be more than one.

$$\vdash\!\!\!\rlap{\raise2pt\hbox{a}}\!\!\!\sqsubset\begin{array}{l} a^4 = 1 \\ a^3 = 1 \end{array};$$

in words: there is at least one cube root of 1 that is also fourth root of 1, or: *some* (at least one) cube root of 1 is fourth root of 1.

In our symbolism the sentence-connective "and" appears less simple than the function-name "$\sqsubset\begin{array}{c}\xi \\ \zeta\end{array}$", for which a simple expression in words is lacking. The relation that obtains in ordinary language seems easily the more natural and appropriate, because we are used to it. What is simpler from a logical standpoint is hard to say: one can define our "$\sqsubset\begin{array}{c}\xi \\ \zeta\end{array}$" by means of "and" and negation; but then conversely, one can define "and" by means of the function-name "$\sqsubset\begin{array}{c}\xi \\ \zeta\end{array}$" and the negation-stroke. Obviously "$\sqsubset\begin{array}{l} 2 + 3 = 5 \\ 2 + 2 = 4 \end{array}$", for example, asserts less than "$\vdash\!\!\!\sqsubset\begin{array}{l} 2 + 3 = 5 \\ 2 + 2 = 4 \end{array}$", hence could be held to be simpler. The real reason for introducing "$\sqsubset\begin{array}{c}\xi \\ \zeta\end{array}$" is the ease and perspicuity with which one can by its use represent deductive inference. To this we now proceed.

---

[21]The *particular* affirmative proposition on the one hand indeed says less than does the *universal* affirmative, but on the other hand (what is easily overlooked) also says more, since it asserts the realization of concepts, whereas subordination occurs also in the case of empty concepts—with the latter, even occurs invariably. Many logicians seem to assume without ado that concepts are realized, and to overlook entirely the very important case of empty concepts, perhaps because they quite wrongly do not recognize empty concepts as justified. This is why I use the expressions "subordination", "universal affirmative", "particular affirmative", in a sense somewhat different from theirs, and arrive at statements that they will be impelled to hold (wrongly) to be false.

§14. First method of inference.

From the propositions " $\models_{\Delta} \Gamma$ " and " $\vdash \Delta$ " we may infer " $\vdash\Gamma$ ";

for if Γ were not the True, then since Δ is the True $\top_{\Delta}\Gamma$ would

be the False. To every proposition set up in signs of Begriffs-schrift that is to be used in a subsequent proof I shall give an *index* for purposes of citation. If the proposition " $\models_{\Delta}\Gamma$ " has

thus received the index "a" and "$\vdash \Delta$" the index "β", then I write the inference either in this way, with a double colon:

$$(\beta):: \frac{\text{“}\quad \models_{\Delta}\Gamma\text{”}}{\vdash\Gamma}\ ,$$

or in this way, with a single colon:

$$(a): \frac{\text{“}\quad \vdash\Delta\text{”}}{\vdash\Gamma}\ .$$

26   This is the sole method of inference used in my book *Begriffs-schrift,* and one can actually manage with it alone. The dictates of scientific economy would properly require that we do so; yet in this book, where I wish to set up lengthy chains of inference, I must make some concessions to practical considerations. In fact, if I were not willing to admit some additional methods of inference the result would be exorbitant lengthiness—a point already anticipated in the Foreword to *Begriffsschrift.*

If we are given the propositions

$$\text{“}\quad \Gamma \quad\text{”} \qquad\text{and}\qquad \text{“}\vdash \Delta\ (\beta\text{”},$$

then we cannot immediately make the inference described above, but only after we have made use of the interchangeability of sub-components, transforming (γ) into

then we cannot immediately make the inference described above, but only after we have made use of the interchangeability of sub-components, transforming (γ) into

But in order to avoid excessive length I do not write it all out

explicitly, but infer directly

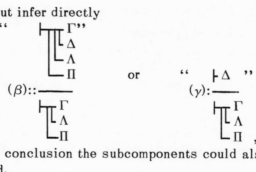

"⊢Γ"

or   " ⊢Δ "

$(\beta)::\underline{\qquad}$ $(\gamma):\underline{\qquad}$

where in the conclusion the subcomponents could also be differently ordered.

If a subcomponent of a proposition differs from a second proposition only in lacking the judgment-stroke, then a proposition may be inferred that results from the first proposition by suppressing that subcomponent.

We also combine two such inferences in a way to be gathered from the following. Let there be given the further proposition "⊢Λ (ρ". Then we write the double inference in this way:

"

$(\beta, \rho)::\overline{\overline{\qquad}}$

15. Second method of inference. Contraposition.

The following method of inference is a little more complicated. From the two propositions

"⊢Γ ∆(a "   and   "⊢Δ Θ(δ "

we may infer the proposition "⊢Γ Θ". For ⊢Γ Θ is the False only

if Θ is the True and Γ is not the True. But if Θ is the True then ∆ too must be the True, for otherwise ∆ Θ would be the False.

But if ∆ is the True then if Γ were not the True then Γ ∆ would   27

be the False. Hence the case of Γ Θ's being the False cannot

arise; and Γ Θ is the True.

58

This inference I write,

either in this way: " $\vdash_{\llcorner \Delta}^{\ulcorner \Gamma}$ ", or in this way: " $\vdash_{\llcorner \Theta}^{\ulcorner \Delta}$ "

$$(\delta)::---$$ $\qquad\qquad\qquad$ $$(a)::---$$

$\vdash_{\llcorner \Theta}^{\ulcorner \Gamma}$ $\qquad\qquad\qquad\qquad\qquad$ $\vdash_{\llcorner \Theta}^{\ulcorner \Gamma}$.

If instead of the proposition (a) we have as premiss the proposition given the index "γ" in §14, then properly we must first transform (γ) as we did there, before making the inference. But for brevity we do this tacitly, as above, writing

" $\vdash\begin{matrix}\ulcorner \Gamma"\\ \Delta\\ \Lambda\\ \Pi\end{matrix}$ " or " $\vdash_{\llcorner \Theta}^{\ulcorner \Delta}$ "

$$(\delta)::---$$ $\qquad\qquad$ $$(\gamma)::---$$

$\vdash\begin{matrix}\ulcorner \Gamma\\ \Theta\\ \Lambda\\ \Pi\end{matrix}$ $\qquad\qquad\qquad$ $\vdash\begin{matrix}\ulcorner \Gamma\\ \Theta\\ \Lambda\\ \Pi\end{matrix}$.

$\vdash_{\llcorner \Gamma}^{\ulcorner \Delta}$ is the False if $-\!\!\!-\ \Gamma$ is the True and $-\!\!\!-\ \Delta$ is not the True; i.e., if $-\!\!\!-\ \Gamma$ is the False and Δ is the True. In all other cases $\top_{\llcorner \Gamma}^{\ulcorner \Delta}$ is the True. But the same holds for $\top_{\llcorner \Delta}^{\ulcorner \Gamma}$; thus the functions $\top_{\llcorner \xi}^{\ulcorner \zeta}$ and $\top_{\llcorner \zeta}^{\ulcorner \xi}$ always have the same value for the same arguments. In the same way the functions $-\!\!\top_{\llcorner \xi}^{\zeta}$ and $-\!\!\top_{\llcorner \zeta}^{\xi}$ always have the same value for the same arguments. We can reduce this case to the previous one by putting "$-\!\!-\ \zeta$" for "ζ" and canceling juxtaposed negation-strokes. The functions $-\!\!\top_{\llcorner \zeta}^{\xi}$ and $-\!\!\top_{\llcorner \xi}^{\zeta}$ also always have the same value for the same arguments. Thus we may pass from the proposition "$\vdash_{\llcorner \Delta}^{\ulcorner \Gamma}$" to the proposition "$\vdash_{\llcorner \Gamma}^{\ulcorner \Delta}$" and conversely. We write these transitions as follows:

59

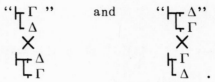

In the same way:

$$\text{"}\vdash\negmedspace\Gamma\text{"} \quad \text{and} \quad \text{"}\vdash\negmedspace\Gamma\text{"}$$

these cases reducing to the first by canceling negation-strokes. We may comprise this in a rule, as follows:

A subcomponent may be interchanged with the main component if the truth-value of each is simultaneously reversed.

This transition we call *contraposition.* But further subcomponents can be present as well; thus we have the transition 28

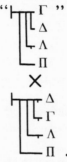

However, by making tacit use of the interchangeability of subcomponents we can also write

By double contraposition we achieve the concentration of all subcomponents into a single one, as follows:

"⊢ Γ"
... (the complex stacked expression)

That is, in the second contraposition we regard

"⊢ Δ"
  Λ
  Π

as main component and "⊤ Γ" as subcomponent. Suppose we give the truth-value

⊢ Δ
  Λ
  Π

the abbreviated name "Θ". Then the next-to-last proposition above becomes "⊢ Θ", from which follows "⊢ Γ". If we then
replace "Θ" by the detailed expression again, we obtain the conclusion. As is to be seen from §12, in

⊢ Δ
  Λ
  Π

we have the truth-value of Δ*'s being the True and* Γ*'s not being the True and* Π*'s being the True.*

If we assume the propositions

"⊢ Γ"   and   "⊢ Λ"
  Δ   Δ
  Λ   Ξ
  Π (γ   Σ (ε

as given, then we may infer as follows: first we concentrate the subcomponents of (ε):

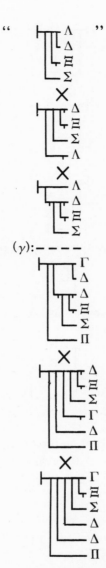

(We may now infer as 29 at the beginning of this §, since this proposition is of the same form as (δ).)

(γ):-----

(Now we unwind again the concentrated sub-component.)

This last we can simplify by writing "Δ" only once:

for

62

$$\vdash\begin{array}{l}\Gamma\\ \llcorner\Delta\\ \llcorner\Delta\end{array}$$

is always the same truth-value as $\vdash\begin{array}{l}\Gamma\\\Delta\end{array}$.

A subcomponent occurring twice need be written only once. This we call the *amalgamation* of identical subcomponents.

I now abbreviate the foregoing transition either in this way: "ε ⊢⊢⊢Λ ", or in this way: "γ ⊢⊢Γ ", and for it I set

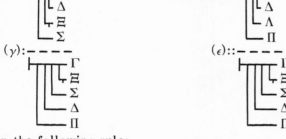

up the following rule:

If the same combination of signs occurs in one proposition as main component and in another as subcomponent, a proposition may be inferred in which the main component of the second is main component, and all subcomponents of either, save the one mentioned, are subcomponents. But subcomponents occurring in both need be written only once.

In a manner like that of §14 we may compress two inferences into one. Let there be given for example, besides (ε), the propositions
"⊢⊢P Θ (θ " and "⊢ Π (η", and "⊢⊢⊢⊢Γ Δ Λ Π P (ι ;

then we may write

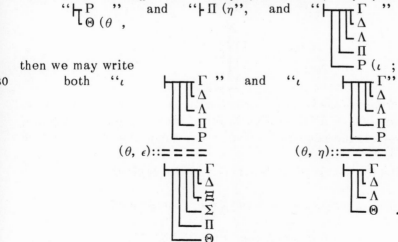

both "ι ⊢⊢⊢⊢Γ Δ Λ Π P " and "ι ⊢⊢⊢⊢Γ Δ Λ Π P"

§16. Third method of inference.

If we assume as given the propositions

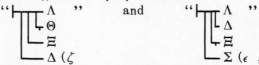

then we can reduce this case to that just treated, namely in this way:

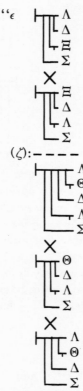

The purpose of the last two contrapositions is to eliminate one occurrence of "— Λ" by amalgamation of identical subcomponents. That ⊤ Λ is the same truth-value as —— Λ can also be understood
   ⊤ Λ
directly; for ⊤ Λ is the False if — Λ is the True and Λ is not the
   ⊤ Λ
True, and otherwise ⊤ Λ is the True. The second condition im-
   ⊤ Λ
plies the first. But —— Λ too is the False if Λ is not the True,

and otherwise ——— Λ is the True. We now abbreviate the fore-going transition in this way:

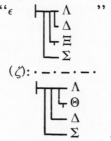

and express the rule as follows:

If two propositions agree in their main components, while a subcomponent of one differs from a subcomponent of the other only in a negation-stroke's being prefixed, then a proposition may be inferred in which the common main component is main component, and all subcomponents of either, save the two mentioned, are subcomponents. Here subcomponents occurring in both need be written only once (amalgamation of identical subcomponents).

§17. Roman letters. Transition from Roman to Gothic letters.

Now let us look to see how the inference called "Barbara" in logic fits into our scheme. From the two sentences,

"All square roots of 1 are fourth roots of 1"

and

"All fourth roots of 1 are eighth roots of 1",

we can infer

"All square roots of 1 are eighth roots of 1".

Now if we write the premisses in this way:

"$\vdash^{a}_{\ a^4 = 1}$"   and   "$\vdash^{a}_{\ a^8 = 1}$"
$a^2 = 1$ $a^4 = 1$,

then we cannot apply our methods of inference. We can, how-ever, it we write them thus:

"$\vdash x^4 = 1$"   and   "$\vdash x^8 = 1$"
$x^2 = 1$ $x^4 = 1$.

Here we have the case of §15. Already earlier [in §8] we made an attempt to express generality in this way by the use of a *Roman letter*, but we left off again, because we observed that the scope of the generality was not well enough demarcated. We now meet this objection by stipulating that in the case of a

65

Roman letter the *scope* shall comprise everything that occurs in the proposition with the exception of the judgment-stroke.[22] Accordingly with a Roman letter we cannot ever express the negation of a generality, but we can express the generality of a negation. Thus no ambiguity is any longer present. However, we see that the expression of generality by Gothic letters and the concavity does not thereby become superfluous. Our stipulation regarding the *scope* of a *Roman letter* is to set only a lower bound upon the scope, not an upper bound. Thus it remains permissible to extend such a scope over several propositions, and this renders the Roman letters suitable to do duty in inferences, which the Gothic letters, with the strict closure of their scopes, cannot. If we have the premises "$\vdash \begin{matrix} x^4 = 1 \\ x^2 = 1 \end{matrix}$" and "$\vdash \begin{matrix} x^8 = 1 \\ x^4 = 1 \end{matrix}$" and infer the proposition "$\vdash \begin{matrix} x^8 = 1 \\ x^2 = 1 \end{matrix}$", in making the transition we extend the scope of the "x" over both of the premises and the conclusion, in order to perform the inference, although each of these propositions still holds good apart from this extension.

Of a Roman letter we say, not that it *denotes* an object, but rather that it *indicates* an object. In the same way we also say that a Gothic letter *indicates* an object, where it does not stand over a concavity.

A proposition with a Roman letter can always be transformed into a proposition with a Gothic letter, whose concavity is separated from the judgment-stroke only by a horizontal. We write such a transition thus:

$$\text{`` } \vdash \Phi(x) \text{ ''}$$

$$\vdash\!\!\cup^{a}\!\!\Phi(a) \ .$$

Here the second rule of §8 should be observed, as in the following example, where "e" may not be chosen as the newly introduced Gothic letter:

---

[22]Here the use of Roman letters is explained only for the case in which there occurs a judgment-stroke. This however is always the case in a development of pure Begriffsschrift; for therein we always proceed directly from one asserted proposition to another asserted proposition.

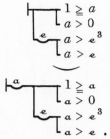

$$\begin{array}{l} 1 \geqq a \\ a > 0 \\ a > e^3 \\ a > e \end{array}$$

$$\begin{array}{l} 1 \geqq a \\ a > 0 \\ a > e^3 \\ a > e \, . \end{array}$$

In connection with the transition from a Roman to a Gothic letter the following case should also be mentioned. Let us consider the proposition "$\vdash \underset{\Gamma}{a} \Phi(a)$", in which "$\Gamma$" is a proper name and "$\Phi(\xi)$" is a function-name. $\underset{\Gamma}{a} \Phi(a)$ is the False if for any argument the function $\underset{\Gamma}{} \Phi(\xi)$ has the False as value. This in turn is the case if Γ is the True, and the value of the function $\longrightarrow \Phi(\xi)$ is for any argument the False. In all other cases $\underset{\Gamma}{a} \Phi(a)$ is the True. Thus "$\vdash \underset{\Gamma}{a} \Phi(a)$" asserts that Γ is not the True, or that the value of the function $\Phi(\xi)$ is the True for every argument. With this let us compare "$\underset{\Gamma}{a} \Phi(a)$". This denotes the False if Γ is the True and $\sim \Phi(a)$ is the False. But the latter is the case if the value of the function $\longrightarrow \Phi(\xi)$ is for any argument the False. In all other cases $\underset{\Gamma}{a} \Phi(a)$ is the True. The proposition "$\vdash \underset{\Gamma}{a} \Phi(a)$" thus asserts the same as does "$\vdash \underset{\Gamma}{a} \Phi(a)$". If for "$\Gamma$" and "$\Phi(\xi)$", combinations of signs are substituted that do not denote an object and a function respectively, but only indicate, because they contain Roman letters, then the foregoing still holds generally if for each Roman letter a name is substituted, whatever this may be.

So as to express myself more accurately, I will introduce the following idiom. I call *names* only such signs and combinations of signs as are to denote something. Thus Roman letters, and combinations of signs in which they occur, are not *names*, because

they only indicate. A combination of signs which contains Roman letters and which always results in a proper name if we replace every Roman letter by a name, I will call a *Roman object-
mark*. And a combination of signs which contains Roman letters
and which always results in a function-name if we replace every Roman letter by a name, I will call a *Roman function-mark*,
or *Roman mark* of a function.

We can now say: the proposition "$\vdash\!\!\!\!\underset{\Gamma}{\overset{a}{}}\Phi(a)$" always asserts
the same as does the proposition "$\vdash\!\!\!\!\underset{\Gamma}{\overset{a}{}}\Phi(a)$", not only if "$\Phi(\xi)$"
is a function-name and "Γ" is a proper name, but also if "$\Phi(\xi)$"
is a Roman function-mark and "Γ" is a Roman object-mark.

Let us apply this to the following case:

$$\begin{array}{l}\vdash \begin{array}{l} a^2 > 4 \\ 2 \cdot a > 4 \end{array} \\ \underset{e}{} \begin{array}{l} e^2 > 4 \\ \underbrace{e} > 2 \end{array} \end{array}$$

$$\underset{e}{\vdash} \begin{array}{l} e^2 > 4 \quad {}^{23} \\ 2 \cdot e > 4 \\ \underset{e}{} \begin{array}{l} e^2 > 4 \\ e > 2. \end{array} \end{array}$$

By the foregoing, for the latter proposition we can also write

$$\underset{e}{\vdash} \begin{array}{l} \underset{e}{} \begin{array}{l} e^2 > 4 \\ 2 \cdot e > 4 \end{array} \\ \underset{e}{} \begin{array}{l} e^2 > 4 \\ e > 2. \end{array} \end{array}$$

Clearly, the only subcomponents which may be left out of the
scope of the newly introduced Gothic letter are those which do
not contain the Roman letter being replaced. I will write such
transitions thus:

$$\text{"}\vdash \begin{array}{l} a^2 > 4 \\ 2 \cdot a > 4 \end{array} \text{"}$$
$$\underset{e}{} \begin{array}{l} e^2 > 4 \\ \underbrace{e} > 2 \end{array}$$

$$\underset{e}{\vdash} \begin{array}{l} e^2 > 4 \\ 2 \cdot e > 4 \\ \underset{e}{} \begin{array}{l} e^2 > 4 \\ e > 2. \end{array} \end{array}$$

Rather than introducing several Gothic letters one after another,

---

[23] The second rule of §8 does not prohibit this iteration of "e", because
"a" in the first proposition does not occur within the scope of "e".

we write the final result straightway under the sign "$\smile$".

We comprise this in the following rule:

A Roman letter may be replaced at all of its occurrences in a proposition by one and the same Gothic letter. The Gothic letter must then at the same time be inserted over a concavity in front of a main component outside which the Roman letter does not oc-cur.[24] *If within this main component is contained the scope of a Gothic letter, and within this scope the Roman letter occurs, then the Gothic letter introduced for the Roman letter must be different from the Gothic letter already present* (second rule of §8).

§18. Laws in symbols of Begriffsschrift (I. IV. VI.).

Now we shall set up, in Roman letters, some general laws that we shall require later. By §12,

$$\begin{array}{c} \Gamma \\ \Delta \\ \Gamma \end{array}$$

could be the False only if both Γ and Δ were the True while Γ was not the True. This is impossible; therefore

$$\begin{array}{c} a \\ b \\ a \end{array} \qquad\qquad (\text{I}$$

The "I" is assigned to this proposition as its index (§14), and indices will be attached to propositions in this way as we proceed. If we write "a" instead of "b", we can amalgamate the identical subcomponents, so that in "$\begin{array}{c} a \\ a \end{array}$" we have a particular case of (I), which will be understood together with (I) without explicit notice.

$\longrightarrow \Delta$ and $\dashv \Delta$ are always different, and always truth-values. Now since $\longrightarrow \Gamma$ is in any case always a truth-value, it must coincide either with $\longrightarrow \Delta$ or with $\dashv \Delta$. It follows from this that $\begin{array}{c}(\longrightarrow \Gamma) = (\longrightarrow \Delta) \\ (\longrightarrow \Gamma) = (\dashv \Delta) \end{array}$ is always the True; for it could be the False only if $\dashv(\longrightarrow \Gamma) = (\dashv \Delta)$ were the True (i.e., if $(\longrightarrow \Gamma) = (\dashv \Delta)$ were the False) and $(\longrightarrow \Gamma) = (\longrightarrow \Delta)$ were not the True (i.e., were the False). In other words, $\begin{array}{c}(\longrightarrow \Gamma) = (\longrightarrow \Delta) \\ (\longrightarrow \Gamma) = (\dashv \Delta) \end{array}$ could

---

[24]Thus if the Roman letter occurs in every subcomponent, then the whole proposition (excluding the judgment-stroke) must be regarded as the main component, and the concavity with the Gothic letter must then be placed separated from the judgment-stroke only by a horizontal.

be the False only if both $(\underline{\quad}\,\Gamma) = (\underline{\quad}\,\Delta)$ and $(\underline{\quad}\,\Gamma) = (\underline{}\!\!\!\tau\, \Delta)$
were the False, which, as we just saw, is not possible. There-
fore

$$\begin{aligned}&(\underline{\quad}\; a) = (\underline{\quad}\; b)\\[-4pt]&(\underline{\quad}\; a) = (\!\!\!\tau\; b)\end{aligned} \qquad\qquad \text{(IV}$$

The brackets to the right of the identity-sign are dispensable.

From the denotation of the function-name $\backslash\xi$ (§11), there follows:

$$\vdash a = \backslash\acute{\epsilon}(a = \epsilon) \qquad\qquad \text{(VI}$$

iv. EXTENSION OF THE NOTATION FOR GENERALITY

§19. Generality with respect to functions. Function-letters. Object-letters.

Up to this point, generality has been expressed only with respect to objects. In order to enable the same for functions, we
distinguish as *function-letters* the letters "*f*", "*g*", "*h*", "*F*",
"*G*", "*H*", and the corresponding Gothic letters: as opposed
to the other letters, which we call *object-letters*,[25] so that the
former shall indicate only functions, and never objects (as object-letters do). Among the object-letters we also reckon the
small Greek vowels, since they occur without the smooth breathing only at places where proper names may also stand. In general after a function-letter there follows within its scope a *brack-
et* whose interior contains either one place, or two separated by
a comma, according as the letter is to indicate a function of one
argument or of two. Such a place serves to receive a simple or
complex sign that denotes or indicates an argument, or occupies
the argument-place in the manner of the small Greek vowels.
Clearly, within its scope a function-letter must occur accompanied everywhere by one argument-place, or everywhere by two.
The *scope* in the case of Roman function-letters comprises everything occurring in the proposition save the judgment-stroke,
and in the case of Gothic letters is demarcated by means of a
concavity with the Gothic letter standing alone. In this, the
use of function-letters wholly agrees with that of object-letters.
We may next consider some illustrative examples.

§20. Laws in symbols of Begriffsschrift (IIa. III. V.).

$\underline{\mathfrak{a}}\,\Phi(\mathfrak{a})$ is the True only if the value of the corresponding function $\Phi(\xi)$ is the True for every argument. Thus in such a case

---

[25] With the exception of "*M*", which is being reserved for a special
purpose.

$\Phi(\Gamma)$ must likewise be the True. It follows that $\underset{a}{\rule{0pt}{0pt}}\Phi(\Gamma)$ is always the True, whatever function of one argument $\Phi(\xi)$ may be. (Here we must observe the first rule of §8, so as to recognize the corresponding function $\Phi(\xi)$. For example, if one were to write "$\underset{a}{\rule{0pt}{0pt}}\Psi(\Gamma, \underset{a}{\rule{0pt}{0pt}}X(\Gamma, a))$", then one could only appear to have names of the same function in the main component and subcomponent. In fact, the subcomponent would be formed by use of the function-name "$\Psi(\xi, \underset{a}{\rule{0pt}{0pt}}X(a, a))$", and the main component by use of the function-name "$\Psi(\xi, \underset{a}{\rule{0pt}{0pt}}X(\xi, a))$".) We now understand by "$\underset{a}{\rule{0pt}{0pt}}\mathfrak{f}(\Gamma)$" the truth-value of *one's always obtaining a name of the True, whatever function-name one may substitute in place of "$\mathfrak{f}$" in "$\underset{a}{\rule{0pt}{0pt}}\mathfrak{f}(\Gamma)$".* This truth-value is the True, whatever object "Γ" may denote: $\vdash\!\!\!\underset{a}{\rule{0pt}{0pt}}\mathfrak{f}(a)$. Since here the concavity with the "$\mathfrak{f}$" is separated from the judgment-stroke only by a horizontal, we may drop the concavity and write a Roman letter in place of the Gothic letter. Thus,

$$\vdash\!\!\!\underset{a}{\rule{0pt}{0pt}}f(a) \tag{IIa}$$

Perhaps we might render this law in words in this way: What holds for all objects, holds also for any.

According to §7 the function of two arguments $\xi = \zeta$ always has as value a truth-value, viz., the True if and only if the ζ-argument coincides with the ξ-argument. If $\Gamma = \Delta$ is the True, then $\underset{\rule{0pt}{0pt}}{f(\Gamma)},\ f(\Delta)$ is also the True; i.e., if Γ is the same as Δ, then Γ falls under every concept under which Δ falls; or, as we may also say: then every statement that holds for Δ holds also for Γ. But also conversely; if $\Gamma = \Delta$ is the False, then not every statement that holds for Δ also holds for Γ, i.e., then $\underset{\rule{0pt}{0pt}}{f(\Gamma)},\ f(\Delta)$ if the False. For example, Γ does not fall under the concept $\xi = \Delta$, under which Δ does fall. Thus, $\Gamma = \Delta$ is always the same truth-value as $\underset{\rule{0pt}{0pt}}{f(\Gamma)},\ f(\Delta)$. Consequently, [the truth-value] $\underset{\rule{0pt}{0pt}}{f(\Gamma)},\ f(\Delta)$ falls under every concept under which [the truth-value] $\Gamma = \Delta$ falls. Thus,

71

$$\left[\begin{matrix} \vdash g\!\left(\overset{\mathfrak{f}}{\frown}\!\!\!\!\begin{array}{l}\\ \end{array}\!\!\begin{array}{l} f(a)\\ f(b)\end{array}\right)\\ g(a=b)\end{matrix}\right.$$
(III

We saw in §§3 and 9 that an identity of courses-of-values may always be transformed into the generality of an identity, and conversely:

$$\vdash (\acute{\epsilon}f(\epsilon) = \acute{a}g(a)) = (\overset{a}{\frown} f(a) = g(a))$$
(V

Here the first rules of §§8 and 9 are to be observed.

§21. Functions and concepts of first and second level.

If we are to give a general explanation of the use of function-letters we require another technical term, which will be explained at this point.

If we consider the names

$$``\overset{a}{\smile} a^2 = 4",\qquad ``\overset{a}{\smile} a > 0",\qquad ``\overset{a}{\underset{\llcorner a\,>\,0}{\smile}} a^2 = 1",$$

then we easily see that we obtain them from "$\overset{a}{\frown} \Phi(a)$"[26] by replacing the function-name "$\Phi(\xi)$" by names of the functions $\xi^2 = 4$, $\xi > 0$, and $\underset{\llcorner \xi\,>\,0}{\ulcorner} \xi^2 = 1$. Clearly, only names of functions of one argument—not proper names, nor names of functions of two arguments—may be substituted, for the combinations of signs being substituted must always have open argument-places to receive the letter "a";[27] and if on the other hand we wanted to substitute a name of a function of *two* arguments, then the ζ-argument-places would remain unfilled. For example, in order to substitute a name of the function $\Psi(\xi, \zeta)$, we might perhaps feel inclined to write "$\overset{a}{\frown} \Psi(a, a)$"; but in that case we should in fact have substituted, not a name of the function $\Psi(\xi, \zeta)$, but rather a name of the function of one argument $\Psi(\xi, \xi)$ (first rule of §8). If we wanted to write "$\overset{a}{\frown} \Psi(a, 2)$", then we should again be substituting only a name of a function of one argument, the function $\Psi(\xi, 2)$. One might perhaps let the "ζ" stand: "$\overset{a}{\frown} \Psi(a, \zeta)$"; here we should have a function whose argument

---

[26] Cf. §13.

[27] That functions (such as $\xi = \xi$ or $\xi^2 - \xi \cdot \xi$) that have the same value for every argument—one might call them constant functions—are nevertheless to be distinguished from this value, this object, itself, I have shown in my essay *Über Function und Begriff*, p. 8.

was indicated by "ζ". We may combine our consideration of this case with the case in which the argument-sign in "$X(\xi)$" is replaced by "$\Phi(\xi)$": "$X(\Phi(\xi))$". We commonly speak here of

37 a 'function of a function', but inaccurately; for if we recall that functions are fundamentally different from objects, and further that the value of a function for an argument is to be distinguished from the function itself, then we see that a function-name can never occupy the place of a proper name, because it carries with it empty places that answer to the unsaturatedness of the function. If we say "the function $\Phi(\xi)$", then we must never forget that "ξ" belongs to the function-name only in the sense that it renders this unsaturatedness recognizable. Thus another function can never occur as argument of the function $X(\xi)$, though indeed the value of a function for an argument can do so: e.g., $\Phi(2)$, in which case the value is $X(\Phi(2))$. If we write "$X(\Phi(\xi))$", then by "$\Phi(\xi)$" we only indicate the argument in the way in which we indicate it in "$X(\xi)$" by "ξ". The function-name is really only a part of "$\Phi(\xi)$", so that the function does not occur here as argument of $X(\xi)$, because the function-name fills up only a part of the argument-place. So too, one c a n n o t say that in "$-\!\!\smile\!\!_{\!-} \Psi(a, \zeta)$" the function-name "$\Psi(\xi, \zeta)$" occupies the place which the function-name "$\Phi(\xi)$" occupies in "$-\!\!\smile\!\!_{\!-} \Phi(a)$"; for it fills up only a part of it, whereas another part, namely the place of the "ζ", is still open for a proper name. *Functions of two arguments* are just as fundamentally different from *functions of one argument* as the latter are from *objects*. For whereas objects are wholly *saturated*, functions of two arguments are saturated to a lesser degree than functions of one argument, which too are already *unsaturated*.

In "$-\!\!\smile\!\!_{\!-} \Phi(a)$", therefore, we have an expression in which we may replace the name of the function $\Phi(\xi)$ by names of functions of one argument, but not by names of objects, and not by names of functions of two arguments. This gives us cause to regard $-\!\!\smile\!\!_{\!-} a^2 = 4$, $-\!\!\smile\!\!_{\!-} a > 0$, and $-\!\!\smile\!\!_{\!\llcorner} a^2 = 1$, as values of the same

function

$$-\!\!\smile\!\!_{\!-} \phi(a)$$

for different *arguments*. Here, however, these arguments are themselves again functions, namely the functions of one argument $\xi^2 = 4$, $\xi > 0$, and $\llcorner \xi^2 = 1$; and only functions of one argument

73

are capable of being arguments of our function $—\overset{a}{\frown}—\phi(a)$. If we say, "the function $—\overset{a}{\frown}—\phi(a)$", then "$\phi$" is a proxy for the sign of an argument, just as "ξ" in the expression "the function $\xi^2 - 4$" is a proxy for a proper name that could appear as sign of an argument. "ϕ" in our present case is not to be assigned to the function any more than "ξ" in the previous case. We now call those functions whose arguments are objects *first-level functions*; on the other hand, those functions whose arguments are first-level functions may be called *second-level functions*. The value of our function $—\overset{a}{\frown}—\phi(a)$ is a l w a y s a truth-value, whatever first-level function we may take as argument. To con- form with earlier nomenclature, we shall accordingly call it a concept: namely a *second-level concept*, to distinguish it from *first-level concepts* which are first-level functions.

Our function $—\overset{a}{\frown}—\phi(a)$ had, for the arguments taken previously, the True as value. If we take now as argument the function $\xi^3 = -1$, $\xi > 0$, then we obtain in $—\overset{a}{\frown}—$ $a^3 = -1$, $a > 0$ the False, because there is no positive cube root of -1. In the same way the value of our function for the argument $\xi + 3$ is the False; for we may always replace $—\overset{a}{\frown}— a + 3$ by $—\overset{a}{\frown}—(\underline{\quad} a + 3)$; and this is the False because the value of the function $\underline{\quad\quad} \xi + 3$ is always the False—if, that is, we assume the plus sign to be so defined that the value of the function $\xi + 3$ is not the True for any argument.

§22. Examples of second-level functions. Unequal-leveled functions and relations.

We have another second-level function in

$$\overset{a\quad e}{\frown\frown}\begin{matrix} a = e \\ \phi(e) \\ \phi(a) \end{matrix} ,$$

where again "ϕ" is a proxy for the sign of the argument. Its value is the True for every first-level concept as argument, under which not more than a single object falls. Accordingly,

$$\vdash\overset{a\quad e}{\frown\frown}\begin{matrix} a = e \\ e + 1 = 3 \\ a + 1 = 3, \end{matrix} \qquad \vdash\overset{a\quad e}{\frown\frown}\begin{matrix} a = e \\ e = e \\ a = a . \end{matrix}$$

On the other hand,

$$\vdash\overset{a\quad e}{\frown\frown}\begin{matrix} a = e \\ e^2 = 1 \\ a^2 = 1 . \end{matrix}$$

We also have a second-level function in $\phi(2)$. The values of this function are in part truth-values, as, for example, for the arguments $\xi + \xi = \xi \cdot \xi$, $\xi + 1 = 4$, to which there correspond the values $2 + 2 = 2 \cdot 2$ and $2 + 1 = 4$, and in part other objects, as, for example, the number 3 for the argument $\xi + 1$. This second-level function is distinct from the number 2 itself, since, like all functions, it is unsaturated.

The second-level function —— $\phi(2)$ is distinguished from the previous function by the fact that its value is always a truth-value. It is thus a second-level concept, which we may call *property of the number 2*; because every concept under which falls the number 2, falls under this second-level concept, and no other first-level functions of one argument fall under this second-level concept. [28]

In

$$\begin{array}{l} \quad\quad\quad \phi(2) \\ \quad\quad a \quad a = 2 \\ \quad\quad\quad \phi(a) \end{array}$$

we also have a second-level concept, which we could call *property of the number 2 that belongs to it exclusively*.

$\underset{a}{\ } \phi(a)$ is also a second-level concept. We have a second-level function that is not a concept in $\acute{\epsilon} \phi(\epsilon)$.

39 In order to have an example from analysis, let us consider the first derivative of a function. We regard the function as argument. If we take a particular function, for example ξ^2, as argument, then we obtain first another first-level function $2 \cdot \xi$; and only if we take an object as argument of this function—for example, the number 3—do we obtain as value an object: the number 6. The first derivative is accordingly to be regarded as a function of two arguments, the first of which must be a first-level function of one argument, the second of which must be an object. On this account we may call it an *unequal-leveled* function of two arguments. From it we obtain a second-level function of one argument if we saturate it with an object-argument—for example, the number 3, i.e., if we determine that the first derivative is to be formed for the argument 3. [29]

[28] Cf. n. 12, above.

[29] It must be presupposed here, as in all of the examples drawn from arithmetic, that the signs of addition, multiplication, and so on, as well as that of the first derivative, have been so defined that a name

We also have an unequal-leveled function of two arguments in $\underline{\quad}\,\phi(\xi)$, where "$\xi$" occupies and renders recognizable the place of the object-argument and "$\phi(\ )$" that of the function-argument. Since the value of this function is always a truth-value, we can call it an unequal-leveled relation. It is the relation of an object to a concept under which it falls.

We have second-level, equal-leveled relations in:

$$\overbrace{\quad}^{a}\begin{array}{l}\phi(a)\\ \psi(a)\end{array}\qquad\text{and}\qquad \overbrace{\quad}^{a}\begin{array}{l}\phi(a)\\ \psi(a)\end{array},$$

where "ϕ" and "ψ" render recognizable the argument-places. In the latter relation, for example, stand the concepts $\xi^3 = 1$ and $\xi^2 = 1$; for we have

$$\vdash\overbrace{\quad}^{a}\begin{array}{l}a^3 = 1\\ a^2 = 1\,;\end{array}$$

in words: at least one square root of 1 is also cube root of 1.

§23. Types of arguments and argument-places. Second-level functions of arguments of type 2 and type 3.

In the examples given hitherto, we have had as arguments functions of one argument. $\overbrace{\quad}^{a\ \ e}\phi(a, e)$ is a second-level concept whose argument must be a function of two arguments. Under this concept there fall all relations such that there are objects which stand in these relations. We can, in fact, mention relations—one might call them empty relations—in which no objects stand to one another; for example, the relation $\begin{array}{l}2\cdot\xi = 2\cdot\zeta\,;\\ \xi = \zeta\end{array}$

for, $\vdash\overbrace{\quad}^{a\ \ e}\begin{array}{l}2\cdot a = 2\cdot e\,.\\ a = e\end{array}$

In order to have another example for this case, let us try to express the *many-oneness* of a relation. By this we understand that for every ξ-argument there exists not more than one ζ-argument such that the value of our function (relation) $X(\xi,\ \zeta)$ for these arguments is the True. We may also say: if from the fact that a stands to b in this relation, and that a stands to c in this relation, it follows universally that b coincides with c, then we say that this relation is many-one. Or: if from the fact that $X(a, b)$ is the True and $X(a, c)$ is the True it follows universally 40

correctly formed out of these together with proper names always has a denotation—which, of course, the customary definitions do not achieve. In them, invariably, only numbers are taken into account, for the most part without saying what a number is.

that $c = b$ is the True, then we call the function $X(\xi, \zeta)$ a many-one relation, if it is a relation at all.

$$\overbrace{\quad e \quad d \quad a \quad}\begin{array}{l} d = a \\ X(e, a) \\ X(e, d) \end{array}$$

must be the True if the relation $\rule{1cm}{0.4pt} X(\xi, \zeta)$ is to be many-one. If we put for "X" the "ϕ" that renders argument places recognizable, we then obtain in

$$\text{``}\overbrace{\quad e \quad d \quad a \quad}\begin{array}{l} d = a \\ \phi(e, a) \\ \phi(e, d) \end{array}\text{''}$$

the name of a second-level function that requires a first-level function of two arguments as argument. This second-level function is a second-level concept under which fall all many-one relations, but also functions $X(\xi, \zeta)$ such that $\rule{1cm}{0.4pt} X(\xi, \zeta)$ is a many-one relation. (The many-oneness is here always intended in the direction from the ξ-argument to the ζ-argument.) If we take as argument of our second-level function the function $\xi^2 = \zeta$, then we obtain as value of the function,

$$\overbrace{\quad e \quad d \quad a \quad}\begin{array}{l} d \; = a \\ e^2 = a \\ e^2 = d \, , \end{array}$$

that is, the True; whereas the False appears as function-value if we take as argument the function $\xi = \zeta^2$:

$$\overbrace{\quad e \quad d \quad a \quad}\begin{array}{l} d = a \quad {}^{30} \\ e = a^2 \\ e = d^2 \, . \end{array}$$

We see from these examples the great multiplicity of functions. We see, too, that there are basically different types of functions, since the various argument-places are basically different. Those argument-places, in fact, that are appropriate for admission of proper names, cannot admit names of functions, and vice versa. Further, those argument-places that may admit names of first-level functions of one argument, are unsuited to admit names of first-level functions of two arguments. Accordingly, we distinguish:

arguments of type 1: objects;
arguments of type 2: first-level functions of one argument;
arguments of type 3: first-level functions of two arguments.

---

[30] With appropriate definition of ξ^2 for arguments that are not numbers.

In the same way we distinguish:

argument-places of type 1, which are appropriate to admit proper names;

argument-places of type 2, which are appropriate to admit names of first-level functions of one argument;

argument-places of type 3, which are appropriate to admit names of first-level functions of two arguments.

Proper names and object-letters are *fitting* for the argument-places of type 1; names of first-level functions of one argument are *fitting* for the argument-places of type 2; names of first-level functions of two arguments are *fitting* for the argument-places of type 3. The objects and functions whose names are fitting for the argument-places of the name of a function, are *fitting* arguments for this function. Functions of one argument for which arguments of type 2 are fitting we call *second-level functions of one argument of type 2;* functions of one argument for which arguments of type 3 are fitting, we call *second-level functions of one argument of type 3.*

Just as in $\underset{a}{\smile} a = a$ we have the value of the second-level function $\underset{a}{\smile} \phi(a)$ for the argument $\xi = \xi$, so too we may regard $\underset{\mathfrak{f}}{\overset{\mathfrak{f}}{\smile}} \begin{bmatrix} \mathfrak{f}(1+1) \\ \mathfrak{f}(2) \end{bmatrix}$ as value of a *third-level function* for the argument $\begin{bmatrix} \phi(1+1) \\ \phi(2) \end{bmatrix}$, which itself is a second-level function of one argument of type 2.

§ 24. General explanation of the use of function-letters.

It is now possible to explain generally the use of function-letters.

If after a concavity with a Gothic function-letter there follows a combination of signs composed of the name of a second-level function of one argument and this function-letter, which fills up the argument-places, then the whole denotes the True if the value of that second-level function is the True for every fitting argument; in all other cases, it denotes the False. Which places are argument-places of the *corresponding* second-level function, is to be decided according to the first rule of §8. Also the second rule of §8 has for function-letters all the validity it has for object-letters.

We have herewith introduced two third-level functions, whose names may be written thus:

41

78

$$\text{``} \underset{\beta}{\text{\small↧}} \mu_\beta(f(\beta)) \text{''} \qquad \text{and} \qquad \text{``} \underset{\beta\gamma}{\text{\small↧}} \mu_{\beta\gamma}(f(\beta, \gamma)) \text{''}$$

in which we render the argument-places recognizable here with "μ_β" and "$\mu_{\beta\gamma}$", just as we render the argument-places of types 2 and 3 recognizable with "ϕ" and "ψ", and of type 1 with "ξ" and "ζ". "μ_β" and "$\mu_{\beta\gamma}$" are, however, no more supposed to be signs of the Begriffsschrift than the former letters, but serve us only provisionally. If we take as arguments for the first-named third-level function the following second-level functions of one argument of type 2, in order:

$$\overset{a}{\text{\small↧}}\phi(a), \qquad \phi(2), \qquad \text{[diagram]}$$

then we obtain as values:

$$\overset{a}{\text{\small↧}}f(a), \qquad \text{\small↧}f(2), \qquad \text{[diagram]}$$

42 ## §25. Generality with respect to second-level functions. Basic Law IIb.

We still require a method of expressing generality with respect to second-level functions of one argument of type 2. One might suppose that this would not nearly suffice; but we shall see that we can make do with this, and that even this occurs only in a single proposition. It may be briefly observed here that this economy is made possible by the fact that second-level functions can be represented in a certain manner by first-level functions, whereby the functions that appear as arguments of the former are represented by their courses-of-values. But the notational device necessary for this does not belong to the primitive notations of the Begriffsschrift; we shall introduce it presently by the use of our primitive signs. Since our means of expression is used only in a single proposition, it is not necessary to explain it in full generality.

We indicate a second-level function of one argument of type 2 in this way:

$$\text{``} M_\beta(\phi(\beta)) \text{''}$$

by using the *Roman function-letter* "M",[31] as we indicate a

---

[31] Thus this letter is not an *object-letter*.

first-level function of one argument by "$f(\xi)$". "$\phi(\ )$" here renders recognizable the argument-place, just as "ξ" does in "$f(\xi)$". The letter "β" here in the brackets fills up the place of the argument of the function occurring as argument [of the whole]. The use of "$M_\beta(\phi(\beta))$" is to second-level functions precisely as the use of "$f(\xi)$" is to first-level functions. We avail ourselves of this expression of generality in the following Basic Law:

$$\left. \begin{array}{l} \text{—} M_\beta(f(\beta)) \\ \text{—} \underset{\mathfrak{f}}{\llcorner} M_\beta(\mathfrak{f}(\beta)) \end{array} \right. \tag{IIb}$$

in words: What holds for all first-level functions of one argument holds also for any. Obviously this Basic Law is for our second-level functions what (IIa) is for first-level functions. "M_β" here corresponds to the letter "f" in (IIa); "f" here corresponds to the "a" in (IIa); and "$\mathfrak{f}$" here corresponds to "$\mathfrak{a}$" in (IIa). Let $\Omega_\beta(\phi(\beta))$ be a second-level function of one argument of type 2, whose place is rendered recognizable by "ϕ". Then $\underset{\mathfrak{f}}{\llcorner}\Omega_\beta(\mathfrak{f}(\beta))$ is the True only if for every fitting argument the value of our s e c o n d - l e v e l function is the True. Then $\Omega_\beta(\Phi(\beta))$ must also be the True. Consequently

$$\left. \begin{array}{l} \text{—} \Omega_\beta(\Phi(\beta)) \\ \text{—} \underset{\mathfrak{f}}{\llcorner} \Omega_\beta(\mathfrak{f}(\beta)) \end{array} \right.$$

is always the True, whatever first-level function of one argument $\Phi(\xi)$ may be, regardless whether $\underset{\mathfrak{f}}{\llcorner}\Omega_\beta(\mathfrak{f}(\beta))$ is the True or the False, and our Basic Law (IIb) asserts this generally for every function of second level of one argument of type 2.

2. DEFINITIONS 43

i. GENERAL REMARKS

§26. Classification of signs. Names. Marks. Proposition of Begriffsschrift. Transition-sign.

The signs explained in the foregoing will now be used for the introduction of new names. But before I enter upon the rules to be observed in such an undertaking, it will aid understanding if I classify our signs and combinations of signs into types and adopt terminology for these.

The Gothic, Roman, and Greek letters occurring in the Begriffsschrift I will not call *names*, because they are not supposed to denote anything. On the other hand I call "$\dot{\smile}\!\!\frac{a}{}\, a = a$", for example, a *name*, because it denotes the True; it is a *proper name*. Thus I call a *proper name*, or *name* of an object, a sign, simple or complex, that is supposed to denote an object, but not a sign that merely indicates an object.

If from a proper name we remove a proper name that forms a part of it or coincides with it, at some or all of the places where the constituent proper name occurs—but in such a way that these places remain recognizable as capable of being filled by one and the same arbitrary proper name (i.e., as being *argument-places of type 1*), then I call that which we obtain by this means a *name* of a first-level function of one argument. Such a name, combined with a proper name filling the argument-place, forms a proper name. Accordingly we have a function-name too in "ξ" itself, provided that the letter "ξ" is only to render recognizable the argument-place. The function named by it has the property that its value for every argument coincides with the argument itself.

If, from a name of a first-level function of one argument, we remove a proper name that forms a part of it, at all or some of the places where it occurs—but in such a way that these places remain recognizable as capable of being filled by one and the same arbitrary proper name (i.e., as being argument-places of type 1), then I call that which we obtain by this means a *name* of a first-level function of two arguments.

If, from a proper name, we remove a name of a first-level function that forms a part of it, at all or some of the places where it occurs—but in such a way that these places remain recognizable as capable of being filled by one and the same arbitrary name of a first-level function (i.e., as being argument-places of type 2 or type 3), then I call that which we obtain by this means a *name* 44 of a second-level function of one argument—an argument of type 2 or type 3, according as the argument-places are of type 2 or type 3.

Names of functions I call for short *function-names*.

It is unnecessary to pursue further these explanations of the types of names.

If, in a proper name, we replace proper names that form a part of it or coincide with it by object-letters, and function-names by function-letters, then I call that which we obtain by this means an *object-mark* or *mark* of an object. If this replacement is by Roman letters only, then I call the mark so obtained a *Roman object-mark*. Thus the object-letters are also object-marks, and the Roman object-letters are Roman object-marks.

A sign (proper name or object-mark) consisting solely of the function-name "$\xi = \zeta$" and proper names or object-marks standing in the two argument-places, I call an *identity*.

If, in a function-name, we replace proper names by object-letters and function-names by function-letters, then I call that which we obtain by this means a *function-mark:* a *mark* of a function of the same kind as that from whose name the mark has been obtained. If this replacement is by Roman letters only, then I call the mark so obtained a *Roman* mark of a function. The function-letters are also function-marks, and the Roman function-letters are Roman function-marks.

The judgment-stroke I reckon neither among the *names* nor among the *marks*; it is a sign of its own special kind. A sign consisting of a judgment-stroke and a name of a truth-value with a horizontal prefixed, I call a *proposition of Begriffsschrift*, or where no doubt can arise, a *proposition*. In the same way, I call *proposition of Begriffsschrift* (or *proposition*) a sign consisting of a judgment-stroke and a Roman mark of a truth-value with a horizontal prefixed.

Signs such as

"(a): ———", "(a, β):: =====", "(a):: ------", "$\times$",

which stand between the propositions so as to indicate the way in which the one below is yielded by the one above, I call *transition-signs*.

§ 27. The double-stroke of definition.

In order now to introduce new signs in terms of those already familiar, we require the *double-stroke of definition,* which appears as an iterated judgment-stroke coupled with a horizontal:
$$\text{"} \| \text{"},$$
and which is used in place of the judgment-stroke where something is to be, not judged, but abbreviated by definition. We introduce a new name by means of a *definition* by stipulating 45 that it is to have the same sense and the same denotation as some name composed of signs that are familiar. Thereby the

82

new sign becomes the same in meaning* as that being used to define it; and thus the definition goes over directly into a proposition. Hence we may cite a definition in the same way as a proposition, in the process replacing the stroke of definition by the judgment-stroke.

A definition is always presented here in the form of an identity with "⊩" prefixed. To the left of the identity-sign we will always write the definiens, and to the right the definiendum. The definiens will be composed of familiar signs.

§28. Correct formation of names.

For definitions I now set up the following leading principle:
Correctly-formed names must always denote something.
I call a name *correctly*-formed, if it consists only of signs introduced as primitive or by definition, and if these signs are used only as what they were introduced as being: thus, proper names as proper names, names of first-level functions of one argument as names of functions of this kind, and so on, so that the argument-places are always filled by fitting names or marks.

To *correct* formation it further appertains, that Gothic and small Greek letters are used only in a way suitable to their purpose.

Thus a Gothic letter may stand over a concavity only if there immediately succeeds this concavity a mark of a truth-value, composed of the name or the mark of a function of one argument together with the same Gothic letter in the argument-places. A function-letter must occur either everywhere in its scope with one argument-place or everywhere with two. A Gothic letter may stand in an argument-place only if there stands to its left a concavity with the same letter, demarcating its scope. Only a Gothic letter may stand over a concavity.

A small Greek vowel may stand under the smooth breathing only if there immediately follows an object-mark, composed of a name or a mark of a first-level function of one argument and of the same Greek letter filling the argument-places. A small Greek vowel may stand in an argument-place only if the same letter precedes it with a smooth breathing, demarcating its scope.

---

wird gleichbedeutend. In view of the previous sentence, it seems best to translate this in the manner of the ordinary German *gleich bedeuten* and not to restrict it to Frege's technical use.

Only a small Greek vowel may occur with the smooth breathing.

§29. When does a name denote something?

Now we answer the question, When does a name denote something? confining ourselves to the following cases.

A name of a first-level function of one argument has a *denota-* *tion* (*denotes* something, succeeds in *denoting*) if the proper name that results from this function-name by its argument-places' being filled by a proper name always has a denotation if the name substituted denotes something.

A proper name has a *denotation* if the proper name that results from that proper name's filling the argument-places of a denoting name of a first-level function of one argument always has a denotation, and if the name of a first-level function of one argument that results from the proper name in question's filling the ξ-argument-places of a denoting name of a first-level function of two arguments always has a denotation, and if the same holds also for the ζ-argument-places.

A name of a first-level function of two arguments has a *denotation* if the proper name that results from this function-name by its ξ-argument-places' being filled by a denoting proper name and its ζ-argument-places' being filled by a denoting proper name always has a denotation.

A name of a second-level function of one argument of type 2 has a *denotation* if, from the fact that the name of a first-level function of one argument denotes something, it follows generally that the proper name that results from its being substituted in the argument-places of our [name of a] second-level function has a denotation.

It follows that every name of a first-level function of one argument which, combined with every denoting proper name, forms a denoting proper name, is also such that if combined with any denoting name of a second-level function of one argument of type 2, it forms a denoting [proper] name.

The name "$\underset{\beta}{\text{\textsmallcaps{ʃ}}}\mu_{\beta}(f(\beta))$" of a third-level function succeeds in denoting, if, from the fact that a name of a second-level function of one argument of type 2 denotes something, it follows generally that the proper name that results from its being substituted in the argument-place of "$\underset{\beta}{\text{\textsmallcaps{ʃ}}}\mu_{\beta}(f(\beta))$" has a denotation.

84

§30. Two ways to form a name.

The foregoing provisions are not to be regarded as definitions of the phrases "have a denotation" or "denote something", because their application always presupposes that we have already recognized some names as denoting. They can serve only in the extension step by step of the sphere of such names. From them it follows that every name formed out of denoting names does denote something. This formation is carried out in this way: a name fills the argument-places of another name that are fitting for it. Thus there arises

[A] a proper name

    [1] from a proper name and a name of a first-level function of one argument,

    or [2] from a name of a first-level function and a name of a second-level function of one argument,

    or [3] from a name of a second-level function of one argument of type 2 and the name "$\underline{}\!\!\!\!\int \mu_\beta(f(\beta))$" of a third-level function;

[B] the name of a first-level function of one argument

    [1] from a proper name and a name of a first-level function of two arguments.

The names so formed may be used in the same way for the formation of further names, and all names arising in this way succeed in denoting if the primitive simple names do so.

A proper name can be employed in the present process of formation only by its filling the argument-places of one of the simple or composite [names of] first-level functions. Composite names of first-level functions arise in the way provided above only from simple names of first-level functions of two arguments by a proper name's filling the ξ- or the ζ-argument-places. Thus the argument-places that remain open in a composite function-name are always also argument-places of a simple name of a function of two arguments. From this it follows that a proper name that is part of a name formed in this way, wherever it occurs, always stands at an argument-place of one of the simple names of first-level functions [of two arguments]. If now we replace this proper name at some or all places by another, then the function-name* so arising is likewise formed in the way

---

*The text has "*Eigenname*" ("proper name"), incorrectly, because the procedure being described does not in this case yield a proper

stated above, and thus it also has a denotation, if all the simple names employed as well succeed in denoting.

Of course in this we are assuming that the simple names of first-level functions of one argument have only one argument-place, and that the simple names of first-level functions of two arguments have only one ξ- and one ζ-argument-place. Otherwise it could indeed occur in the case of the replacement just described that related argument-places of simple function-names were filled by different names, and an explanation of the denotation for this case would be lacking. But this can always be avoided: and must be avoided, so as to prevent the occurrence of denotationless names. And there would certainly be no point in introducing several ξ-argument-places or several ζ-argument-places into the simple function-names.

On this assumption, then, we see the possibility of a second procedure for forming names of first-level functions. To wit: we begin by forming a name in the first way, and we then exclude from it at all or some places, a proper name that is a part of it (or coincides with it entirely)—but in such a way that these places remain recognizable as argument-places of type 1. The function-name resulting from this likewise always has a denotation if the simple names from which it is formed denote something; and it may be used further to form denoting names in the first way or in the second.

Thus, for example, in the first way we can form, from the proper name "Δ" and the function-name "$\xi = \zeta$", the function-name   48 "$\Delta = \zeta$", and further from the latter name and "Δ", the proper name "$\Delta = \Delta$". In the second way we form from "$\Delta = \Delta$" the function-name "$\xi = \xi$", and then in the first way, from this and the function-name "$\underset{\alpha}{\smile}\ \phi(\alpha)$", form the proper name "$\underset{\alpha}{\smile}\ a = a$".

All correctly-formed names are formed in this manner.

---

name. The point being introduced is this. If, in a denoting 'composite' expression "$\Phi(\Delta)$" or "$\Phi(\Delta,\ \zeta)$", containing a constituent proper name "Δ", replacement of that proper name by a proper name always results in an expression having denotation provided that the name substituted has a denotation, then the result of removing "Δ", i.e. "$\Phi(\xi)$" or "$\Phi(\xi,\ \zeta)$", may be called a name having denotation. This procedure of forming a name is the 'second way'. The special case at this point is of the type "$\Phi(\Delta,\ \zeta)$". Two paragraphs below, it is of the other type, "$\Phi(\Delta)$" (specifically, "$\Delta = \Delta$").

31. Our simple names denote something.

Let us apply the foregoing in order to show that the proper names, and names of first-level functions, which we can form in this way out of our simple names introduced up to now, always have a denotation. By what has been said, it is necessary to this end only to demonstrate of our primitive names that they denote something. These are

1. names of first-level functions of one argument,
$$`` \text{---}\ \xi \text{''}, \qquad `` \text{---}\hspace{-1pt}\text{r}\ \xi \text{''}, \qquad `` \backslash \xi \text{''};$$

2. names of first-level functions of two arguments,
$$`` \underset{\zeta}{\mathsf{L}}{\xi} \text{''} \qquad `` \xi = \zeta \text{''};$$

3. names of second-level functions of one argument of type 2,
$$`` \underset{}{\text{---}^{a}}\ \phi(a) \text{''}, \qquad `` \acute{\epsilon}\ \phi(\epsilon) \text{''};$$

4. names of third-level functions,
$$`` \underset{\beta}{\text{---}\!f}\ \mu_{\beta}(\mathit{f}(\beta)) \text{''}, \qquad `` \underset{\beta\gamma}{\text{---}\!f}\ \mu_{\beta\gamma}(\mathit{f}(\beta,\ \gamma)) \text{''},$$

    of which the last may be left out of account because it will not actually be used.

First let it be noted that there always occurs only one ξ- and only one ζ-argument-place. We start from the fact that the names of truth-values denote something, namely, either the True or the False. We then gradually widen the sphere of names to be recognized as succeeding in denoting by showing that those to be adopted, together with those already adopted, form denoting names by way of the one's appearing at fitting argument-places of the other.

In order now to show, first, that the function-names "$\text{---}\ \xi$" and "$\text{---}\hspace{-1pt}\text{r}\ \xi$" denote something, we have only to show that those names succeed in denoting that result from our putting for "ξ" a name of a truth-value (we are not yet recognizing other objects). This follows immediately from our explanations. The names obtained are again names of truth-values.

If in the function-names "$\underset{\zeta}{\mathsf{L}}{\xi}$" and "$\xi = \zeta$" we put names of truth-values for "ξ" and for "ζ", then we obtain names that denote truth-values. Consequently our names of first-level functions of two arguments have denotations.

To investigate whether the name "$\text{---}^{a}\ \phi(a)$" of a second-level function denotes something, we ask whether it follows universally

49

87

from the fact that the function-name "$\Phi(\xi)$" denotes something, that "$\unicode{x2013}^{a}\, \Phi(a)$" succeeds in denoting. Now "$\Phi(\xi)$" has a denotation if, for every denoting proper name "Δ", "$\Phi(\Delta)$" denotes something. If this is the case, then this denotation either always is the True (whatever "Δ" denotes), or not always. In the first case "$\unicode{x2013}^{a}\, \Phi(a)$" denotes the True, in the second the False. Thus it follows universally from the fact that the substituted function-name "$\Phi(\xi)$" denotes something, that "$\unicode{x2013}^{a}\, \Phi(a)$" denotes something. Consequently the function-name "$\unicode{x2013}^{a}\, \phi(a)$" is to be admitted into the sphere of denoting names. The same follows similarly for "$\unicode{x2013}^{\ell}_{\beta}\, \mu_{\beta}(\ell(\beta))$".

The matter is less simple with "$\acute{\epsilon}\phi(\epsilon)$"; for with this we are introducing not merely a new function-name, but simultaneously answering to every name of a first-level function of one argument, a new proper name (course-of-values-name); in fact not just for those [function-names] known already, but in advance for all such that may be introduced in the future. To the inquiry whether a course-of-values-name denotes something, we need only subject such course-of-values-names as are formed from denoting names of first-level functions of one argument. We shall call these for short *fair** course-of-values-names. We must examine whether a fair course-of-values-name placed in the argument-places of "$\underline{\quad}\,\xi$" and "$\rlap{\,\unicode{x2013}}{\top}\,\xi$" yields a denoting proper name, and further whether, placed in the ξ-argument-places or in the ζ-argument-places of "$\underset{\zeta}{\rule[-0.6em]{0.5pt}{1.2em}\!\!\rule{0.6em}{0.5pt}}\,\xi$" and "$\xi = \zeta$", it always forms

a denoting name of a first-level function of one argument. If we substitute the course-of-values-name "$\acute{\epsilon}\Phi(\epsilon)$" for "$\zeta$" in "$\xi = \zeta$", then the question is thus whether "$\xi = \acute{\epsilon}\Phi(\epsilon)$" is a denoting name of a first-level function of one argument, and to that end it is to be asked in turn whether all proper names denote something that result from our putting in the argument-place either a name of a truth-value or a fair course-of-values-name. By our stipulations, that "$\acute{\epsilon}\Psi(\epsilon) = \acute{\epsilon}\Phi(\epsilon)$" is always to have the same denotation as "$\unicode{x2013}^{a}\, \Psi(a) = \Phi(a)$", that "$\acute{\epsilon}(\underline{\quad}\,\epsilon)$" is to denote the True, and that "$\acute{\epsilon}(\epsilon = \unicode{x2013}^{a}\, a = a)$" is to denote the False, a denotation is assured in every case for a proper name of the form "$\Gamma = \Delta$", if "Γ" and "Δ" are fair course-of-values-names or

rechte.

88

names of truth-values. Thereby it is also known that we always obtain a denoting proper name from the function-name "$\xi = (\xi = \xi)$", if we put in the argument-places a fair course-of-values-name. Since now according to our stipulations the function —— ξ always has the same value for the same argument as the function $\xi = (\xi = \xi)$, it is also known of the function-name "—— ξ" that a proper name of a truth-value always results from it by substitution of a fair course-of-values-name. By our stipulations the names "$\twoheadrightarrow \Delta$" and "$\underset{\Delta}{\mathrel{\rule[0.3em]{0.6em}{0.4pt}\!\!\rule{0.4pt}{0.8em}}}\Gamma$" always have denotations if the names "—— Δ" and "—— Γ" denote something. Since this is now the case if "Γ" and "Δ" are fair course-of-values-names, we always obtain denoting proper names from the function-names "$\twoheadrightarrow \xi$" and "$\underset{\zeta}{\mathrel{\rule[0.3em]{0.6em}{0.4pt}\!\!\rule{0.4pt}{0.8em}}}\xi$" by placing fair course-of-values-names or names of truth-values in the argument-places. We have seen that each of our simple names of first-level functions "—— ξ", "$\twoheadrightarrow \xi$", "$\underset{\zeta}{\mathrel{\rule[0.3em]{0.6em}{0.4pt}\!\!\rule{0.4pt}{0.8em}}}\xi$", "$\xi = \zeta$", up to now recognized as denoting, produces denoting names upon admission of fair course-of-values-names in the argument-places. Thus the fair course-of-values-names may be admitted into our sphere of denoting names. Thereby, however, the same thing is decided for our function-name "$\acute{\epsilon}\phi(\epsilon)$", since it now follows universally from the fact that a name of a first-level function of one argument denotes something, that the proper name resulting from its being substituted in "$\acute{\epsilon}\phi(\epsilon)$" denotes something.

From among our primitive names there now remains only "$\backslash\xi$". We have determined that "$\backslash\Delta$" shall denote Γ, if [there exists an object Γ such that] "Δ" is a name of the course-of-values $\acute{\epsilon}(\epsilon = \Gamma)$, and that on the other hand "$\backslash\Delta$" shall denote Δ, if there exists no object Γ such that "Δ" is a name of the course-of-values $\acute{\epsilon}(\epsilon = \Gamma)$. By this a denotation is assured for all cases for a proper name of the form "$\backslash\Delta$" and therewith for the function-name "$\backslash\xi$".

§ 32. Every proposition of Begriffsschrift expresses a thought.

In this way it is shown that our eight primitive names have denotation, and thereby that the same holds good for all names correctly compounded out of these. However, not only a denotation, but also a sense, appertains to all names correctly formed from our signs. Every such name of a truth-value *expresses* a sense, a *thought*. Namely, by our stipulations it is determined under what conditions the name denotes the True. The sense of this name—the *thought*—is the thought that these conditions are fulfilled. Now a proposition of Begriffsschrift consists of the judgment-stroke and of a name or a Roman mark of a truth-value. (But such a mark is transformed into the name of a truth-value by the introduction of Gothic letters in place of Roman letters and the prefixing of concavities according to §17. If we imagine this carried out, then we have only the case in which the proposition is composed of the judgment-stroke and a name of a truth-value.) It is now asserted by such a proposition that this name does denote the True. Since at the same time it expresses a thought, we have in every correctly-formed proposition of Begriffsschrift a judgment that a thought is true; and here 51 a thought certainly cannot be lacking. It will be the reader's task to make clear to himself the thought of each proposition of Begriffsschrift, and I shall take pains to facilitate this as much as possible at the outset.

The names, whether simple or themselves composite, of which the name of a truth-value consists, contribute to the expression of the thought, and this contribution of the individual [component] is its *sense*. If a name is part of the name of a truth-value, then the sense of the former name is part of the thought expressed by the latter name.

§33. Principles of definition.

The following are our standard principles for definitions:

1. Every name correctly formed from the defined names must have a denotation. Thus it must always be possible to produce a name, compounded out of our eight primitive names, that is the same as it in meaning*, and the latter must be unambiguously determined by the definitions, up to inessential choices of particular Gothic and Greek letters.

2. It follows from this that the same thing may never be defined twice, because it would then remain in doubt whether these definitions were consistent with one another.

3. The name defined must be simple; that is, it may not be composed of any familiar names or names that are yet to be defined; for o t h e r w i s e it would remain in doubt whether the

---

Gleichbedeutend ist. Cf. translator's note, p. 83, above.

definitions of the names were consistent with one another.

4. If on the left-hand side of the definitional identity we have a proper name formed from our primitive names or defined names, then this always has a denotation, and we shall place on the right-hand side a simple sign not previously employed, which is now introduced by the definition as a proper name having the same meaning*, so that we may in future replace this sign wherever it occurs by the name standing on the left. Of course this sign may never be used as a function-name, for to do so would be to cut off the route back to the primitive names.

5. A name introduced for a first-level function of one argument may contain only a single argument-place. With more argument-places it would be possible to fill these with different names, and then the name defined would be being used as the name of a function of more than one argument, whereas it would not be defined as such. If a name of a first-level function of one argument is defined, the argument-places on the left-hand side of the definitional identity must be filled with one Roman object-letter, which also renders recognizable the argument-place of the new function-name on the right-hand side. The definition then asserts that the proper name that results on the right-hand side from substitution of a denoting proper name in the argument-place, shall always have the same meaning** as that which results on the left-hand side from substitution of the same proper name in all argument-places. The one argument-place of the name defined thus represents all those of the definiens. Wherever the defined name may occur subsequently, its argument-place must always be filled by a proper name or an object-mark.

6. A name introduced for a first-level function of two arguments must contain two and only two argument-places. The mutually related argument-places on the left-hand side must be occupied by one and the same Roman object-letter, which also renders recognizable one of the two argument-places on the right-hand side; argument-places that are not related must contain different Roman letters. The definition then asserts that the proper name which results on the right-hand side from substitution of denoting proper names in the argument-places, shall

----

*Gleichbedeutend. Cf. the previous note.
**Gleichbedeutend sein.

always have the same meaning* as that which results on the left-hand side from substitution of the same proper names in the corresponding argument-places. One argument-place on the right-hand side thus represents all the ξ-argument-places on the left-hand side, and the other represents all the ζ-argument-places.

7. Thus there must never occur on one side of a definitional identity a Roman letter that does not occur on the other. If the object-mark on the left-hand side is transformed into a correctly-formed proper name, by the Roman letters' being replaced by proper names, then by our stipulations the function-name defined always has a denotation.

Cases other than those just mentioned will not occur in the sequel.

ii. PARTICULAR DEFINITIONS

§ 34. Definition of the function $\xi \cap \zeta$.

It has already been suggested, in §25, that in further developments, instead of second-level functions, we may employ first-level functions. This will now be shown. As was indicated then, this is made possible through the functions that appear as arguments of second-level functions being represented by their courses-of-values—though of course not in such a way that they simply give up their places to them, for that is impossible.

In the first instance it is a matter only of designating the value of the function $\Phi(\xi)$ for the argument Δ, i.e., $\Phi(\Delta)$, by means of "Δ" and "$\acute{\epsilon}\Phi(\epsilon)$". I do so in this way:

$$\text{"}\Delta \cap \acute{\epsilon}\Phi(\epsilon)\text{"},$$

which is to mean the same as* "$\Phi(\Delta)$". The object $\Phi(\Delta)$ thus appears as the value of the function of two arguments $\xi \cap \zeta$ for Δ as ξ-argument and $\acute{\epsilon}\Phi(\epsilon)$ as ζ-argument.

But $\xi \cap \zeta$ must now be defined for all possible objects as argu- 5: ments. This may be done as follows:

$$\vdash \backslash\overset{2}{a}\left(\underset{\quad\quad\ u\,=\,\acute{\epsilon}\,q(\epsilon)}{\overset{q}{\rule{0pt}{1em}}}\,q(a)\,=\,a\right)\,=\,a\cap u \tag{A}$$

Since here a function of two arguments is being defined, two Roman letters occur on both the left- and the right-hand side. Although the definiens contains only familiar notation, a few explanatory remarks are in order. We have on the left-hand side

---

*Gleichbedeutend sein.

92

a Roman mark, which results from the proper name
" $\backslash\grave{a}\left(-\underset{\llcorner\Gamma\,=\,\acute{\epsilon}\,\mathfrak{g}(\epsilon)}{\overset{\mathfrak{g}}{\frown}}\mathfrak{g}(\Theta)=a\right)$ " by substitution of "a" for "Θ" and "u"
for "Γ". This proper name has the form "$\backslash\grave{a}\Phi(a)$". With it, by
§11, there are two cases to distinguish, according as one can
find an object Δ that and that alone falls under the concept
$——\Phi(\xi)$, or not. In the first case $\backslash\grave{a}\Phi(a)$ is Δ itself. Applied
to our case, this means that if there exists an object Δ such
that $-\underset{\llcorner\Gamma\,=\,\acute{\epsilon}\,\mathfrak{g}(\epsilon)}{\overset{\mathfrak{g}}{\frown}}\mathfrak{g}(\Theta)=\Delta$ is the True, whereas the function
$-\underset{\llcorner\Gamma\,=\,\acute{\epsilon}\,\mathfrak{g}(\epsilon)}{\overset{\mathfrak{g}}{\frown}}\mathfrak{g}(\Theta)=\xi$ has the False as value for all arguments other
than Δ, then Δ itself is $\backslash\grave{a}\left(-\underset{\llcorner\Gamma\,=\,\acute{\epsilon}\,\mathfrak{g}(\epsilon)}{\overset{\mathfrak{g}}{\frown}}\mathfrak{g}(\Theta)=a\right)$. Now, $-\underset{\llcorner\Gamma\,=\,\acute{\epsilon}\mathfrak{g}(\epsilon)}{\overset{\mathfrak{g}}{\frown}}\mathfrak{g}(\Theta)=\Delta$
is the True if there exists a first-level function of one argu-
ment whose value for the argument Θ is Δ and whose course-of-
values is Γ. Otherwise $-\underset{\llcorner\Gamma\,=\,\acute{\epsilon}\,\mathfrak{g}(\epsilon)}{\overset{\mathfrak{g}}{\frown}}\mathfrak{g}(\Theta)=\Delta$ is the False. If we assume that Γ is a course-of-values, then by [choice of] Γ it is
determined what value a function has, whose course-of-values
is Γ, for the argument Θ. In that case there exists one and only
one such value, and this value is $\backslash\grave{a}\left(-\underset{\llcorner\Gamma\,=\,\acute{\epsilon}\,\mathfrak{g}(\epsilon)}{\overset{\mathfrak{g}}{\frown}}\mathfrak{g}(\Theta)=a\right)$, or $\Theta\cap\Gamma$.

If, however, Γ is not a course-of-values, then the function
$-\underset{\llcorner\Gamma\,=\,\acute{\epsilon}\,\mathfrak{g}(\epsilon)}{\overset{\mathfrak{g}}{\frown}}\mathfrak{g}(\Theta)=\xi$ has the False as value for every argument, and
in that case our stipulation is to be drawn upon, that "$\backslash\Lambda$" is
to denote Λ itself if there exists no object Δ such that Λ is the
course-of-values $\acute{\epsilon}(\Delta=\epsilon)$. Accordingly, if Γ is not a course-of-
values, "$\Theta\cap\Gamma$" denotes the course-of-values of a function
whose value for every argument is the False: thus, $\acute{\epsilon}(-\!\!\top\!\epsilon=\epsilon)$.

To recapitulate, two cases must be distinguished if the value
of the function $\xi\cap\zeta$ is to be fully determined. If the ζ-argument
is a course-of-values, then the value of the function $\xi\cap\zeta$ is the
value, for the ξ-argument as argument, of the function whose
course-of-values is the ζ-argument. If on the other hand the ζ-
argument is not a course-of-values, then the value of the func-
tion $\xi\cap\zeta$ for any ξ-argument is $\acute{\epsilon}(-\!\!\top\!\epsilon=\epsilon)$.

§35. Representation of second-level functions by first-level functions.

Here we see confirmed, what we could gather from considerations already set out, that the function-name "$\xi \cap \zeta$" has a denotation. Only this is fundamental to the forthcoming conduct of proofs; our elucidation could be wrong in other respects without placing the correctness of those proofs in question; for only the definition itself is the foundation for this edifice. The definition is supposed to serve, as we said at the outset, to enable first-level functions to be applied in place of second-level functions. Let us see in some examples how this purpose is achieved. In §22 we cited the second-level function $\phi(2)$. Now for "$\phi(2)$" we can write "$2 \cap \acute{\epsilon} \phi(\epsilon)$". This is still the name of a second-level function; but if we write "ξ" for "$\acute{\epsilon} \phi(\epsilon)$", then we have in "$2 \cap \xi$" the name of a first-level function. The function $\phi(2)$ has for the function $\Phi(\xi)$ as argument the same value as has the function $2 \cap \xi$ for $\acute{\epsilon}\Phi(\epsilon)$ as argument: that is, $\Phi(2)$. If as argument of the function $2 \cap \xi$ an object is taken that is not a course-of-values, then we have no corresponding argument of the second-level function $\phi(2)$, and the reciprocal representability of the two functions, of first and second level, ceases.

To the second-level functions

$$\underset{a}{\smallfrown}\!\!\!\!\!\!\frown \phi(a) \qquad \text{and} \qquad$$

there correspond in the same way the first-level functions

$$\underset{a}{\smallfrown}\!\!\!\!\!\!\frown a \cap \xi \qquad \text{and} \qquad$$

§36. The double course-of-values. The extension of a relation.

So as to find other examples, let us try to arrange the representation of functions of two arguments by objects, in a way similar to that used for functions of one argument. Of course a simple course-of-values cannot be used to this end, but only a double course-of-values, which is to a function of two arguments what a simple course-of-values is to a function of one argument.

Let us proceed by way of examples from the function of two arguments $\xi + \zeta$. If we take as ζ-argument the number 3, for example, then we still have in $\xi + 3$ a function of one argument, whose course-of-values is $\acute{\epsilon}(\epsilon + 3)$. A corresponding feature holds for every ζ-argument, and we have in $\acute{\epsilon}(\epsilon+\zeta)$ a function of one argument, whose value is always a course-of-values. If we imagine the ξ- and the ζ-argument, and the value of the function $\xi+\zeta$, represented as rectilinear coördinates in space, then we can illustrate the course-of-values $\acute{\epsilon}(\epsilon+3)$ by a straight line. If we allow the ζ-argument to vary uniformly, then this straight line is placed in motion and describes a plane. At each of its positions it illustrates a course-of-values, the value of the function $\acute{\epsilon}(\epsilon+\zeta)$ for a certain ζ-argument. Now the course-of-values

55 of the function $\acute{\epsilon}(\epsilon+\zeta)$ is $\grave{a}\acute{\epsilon}(\epsilon+a)$, and this I call a *double course-of-values*. Now,

$$\Delta \cap \grave{a}\acute{\epsilon}(\epsilon+a) = \acute{\epsilon}(\epsilon+\Delta)$$

is the True, and so is

$$\Gamma \cap (\Delta \cap \grave{a}\acute{\epsilon}(\epsilon+a)) = \Gamma \cap \acute{\epsilon}(\epsilon+\Delta),$$

and since

$$\Gamma \cap \acute{\epsilon}(\epsilon+\Delta) = \Gamma + \Delta$$

is the True,

$$\Gamma \cap (\Delta \cap \grave{a}\acute{\epsilon}(\epsilon+a)) = \Gamma + \Delta$$

is also the True. Here on the left-hand side we see a double course-of-values representing the function of two arguments [whose name occurs] on the right-hand side—of course, not in such a way that what represents simply takes over the place of what is represented, for that is impossible, but only in this way: in the double course-of-values [whose name occurs] on the left-hand side is captured what is peculiar to the function [whose name occurs] on the right-hand side, what distinguishes it from other first-level functions of two arguments. If the function of two arguments is a relation, we may say for "double course-of-values" also "*extension* of the relation".

One may still ask what $\Gamma \cap (\Delta \cap \Theta)$ is to be if Θ is not a double course-of-values but instead either a simple course-of-values or not a course-of-values at all. In the first case $\Delta \cap \Theta$ is not a course-of-values, and consequently $\Gamma \cap (\Delta \cap \Theta)$ is the same as $\acute{\epsilon}(\frac{}{\top} \epsilon = \epsilon)$. In the other case, $\Delta \cap \Theta$ coincides with $\acute{\epsilon}(\frac{}{\top} \epsilon = \epsilon)$, and

$$\Gamma \cap (\Delta \cap \Theta) = \Gamma \cap \acute{\epsilon}(\frac{}{\top} \epsilon = \epsilon)$$

is the True; and so $\Gamma \cap (\Delta \cap \Theta) = (\frac{}{\top} \Gamma = \Gamma)$ is also the True; i.e., $\Gamma \cap (\Delta \cap \Theta)$ is in that case the False.

§37. Definition of the function $I\xi$.

In place of the second-level function

$$\overbrace{}^{e\quad d}\quad\overbrace{}^{a}\; \begin{array}{l} d = a \\ \phi(e,\,a) \\ \phi(e,\,d) \end{array}$$

(§23), we can now consider the first-level function

$$\overbrace{}^{e\quad d}\quad\overbrace{}^{a}\; \begin{array}{l} d = a \\ e\cap(a\cap\xi) \\ e\cap(d\cap\xi)\,. \end{array}$$

We introduce a simple notation for this, by defining as follows:

$$\Vdash\left(\overbrace{}^{e\quad d}\quad\overbrace{}^{a}\; \begin{array}{l} d = a \\ e\cap(a\cap p) \\ e\cap(d\cap p) \end{array}\right) = Ip$$

$$(\Gamma$$

By §23,

$$\overbrace{}^{e\quad d}\quad\overbrace{}^{a}\; \begin{array}{l} d = a \\ e\cap(a\cap\Delta) \\ e\cap(d\cap\Delta) \end{array}$$

is the truth-value of *the relation* $——\,\xi\cap(\zeta\cap\Delta)$*'s being many-one;* i.e., for every ξ-argument there being either no ζ-argument, or only one, for which the value of our function is the True, or, as we can also say, for every object there being at most one object to which it stands in the relation $——\,\xi\cap(\zeta\cap\Delta)$. If Δ is not a double course-of-values, then by §36 the value of the function $——\,\xi\cap(\zeta\cap\Delta)$ is either the False or else $\grave{e}(\,{-}_{\top}\,\epsilon = \epsilon)$. Since this last is not the True, the value of the function $——\,\xi\cap(\zeta\cap\Delta)$ is always the False if Δ is not a double course-of-values; i.e., then $——\,\xi\cap(\zeta\cap\Delta)$ is a relation in which no object stands to any object. In such a case $I\Delta$ is the True. We are introducing the function-name "$I\xi$" particularly with a view to the cases in which the extension of a relation appears as argument. If this relation is $X(\xi,\,\zeta)$, then $I\grave{a}\grave{e}X(\epsilon,\,a)$ is the True if the relation $X(\xi,\,\zeta)$ is many-one (going from the ξ- to the ζ-argument). Thus, for example, $\vdash I\grave{a}\grave{e}(\epsilon^2 = a)$. By our definition, "I" may be used only as a functional sign that precedes the argument-sign or a proxy for it.

§38. Definition of the function $)\xi$.

Now we can draw closer to our goal, the definition of number. in my *Grundlagen der Arithmetik* I based this definition on the relation that I called 'equinumeracy'. The definition of the

56

96

latter offered in §72 (p. 85) of my *Grundlagen* is:

The expression

"the concept F is equinumerate with the concept G"

is to mean the same as* the expression

"there exists a relation ϕ that correlates one to one the objects falling under the concept F with the objects falling under the concept G".

Now what is it for the relation ϕ to correlate the objects falling under the concept F with those falling under the concept G? It is, (§71 of *Grundlagen*) for every object that falls under F to stand in the relation ϕ to an object falling under the concept G, or more accurately, that the two propositions

"a falls under F"

and

"a does not stand in the relation ϕ to any object falling under G"

cannot hold simultaneously for any a.

We now take as concept F, $— \xi \cap \Gamma$; and as concept G, $— \xi \cap \Delta$; and as relation ϕ, $— \xi \cap (\zeta \cap \mathrm{T})$. Then we can express the foregoing in signs of Begriffsschrift thus:

$$\underset{a}{\overset{d}{\vphantom{|}}}\begin{array}{l} d \cap \Gamma \qquad {}^{32}\\ a \cap \Delta \\ d \cap (a \cap \mathrm{T}). \end{array}$$

The relation must be many-one. If we add this condition, we have

$$\underset{a}{\overset{d}{\vphantom{|}}}\begin{array}{l} d \cap \Gamma \\ a \cap \Delta \\ d \cap (a \cap \mathrm{T}) \\ \mathrm{IT} \end{array}$$

(On "and", cf. §12.) We regard this as value of the function of two arguments

$$\underset{a}{\overset{d}{\vphantom{|}}}\begin{array}{l} d \cap \xi \\ a \cap \zeta \\ d \cap (a \cap \mathrm{T}) \\ \mathrm{IT} \end{array}$$

Sei gleichbedeutend. In this case the rendering is justified by the fact that Frege is quoting from *Grundlagen*, where "*bedeuten*" is not used in the special sense that he subsequently gave it. Cf. Austin's note to his translation of *Grundlagen*, p. i.

[32] Here "d" corresponds to "a" of the expression in words.

for the arguments Γ and Δ. This function is a relation. Its double course-of-values is

$$\grave{a}\grave{\epsilon}\left[\quad\begin{array}{l}d \cap \epsilon\\ a \cap a\\ d \cap (a \cap \mathrm{T})\\ \mathrm{IT}\end{array}\right].$$

We regard the last as value of the function

$$\grave{a}\grave{\epsilon}\left[\quad\begin{array}{l}d \cap \epsilon\\ a \cap a\\ d \cap (a \cap \xi)\\ \mathrm{I}\xi\end{array}\right]$$

for the argument T. For this function we introduce a brief name by means of the following definition:

$$\Vdash \grave{a}\grave{\epsilon}\left[\quad\begin{array}{l}d \cap \epsilon\\ a \cap a\\ d \cap (a \cap p)\\ \mathrm{I}p\end{array}\right] = \rangle p \tag{Δ}$$

The value of this function is always the extension of a relation. What now is $\Gamma \cap (\Delta \cap \rangle\mathrm{T})$? By the definition,

$$\Gamma \cap \left[\Delta \cap \grave{a}\grave{\epsilon}\left[\quad\begin{array}{l}d \cap \epsilon\\ a \cap a\\ d \cap (a \cap \mathrm{T})\\ \mathrm{IT}\end{array}\right]\right]$$

is to be substituted for this, or

$$\begin{array}{l}d \cap \Gamma\\ a \cap \Delta\\ d \cap (a \cap \mathrm{T})\\ \mathrm{IT}\end{array}\quad.$$

5

This is the truth-value of *the relation* $\xi \cap (\zeta \cap \mathrm{T})$'s *correlating many-one the objects falling under the concept* $\xi \cap \Gamma$ *with objects falling under the concept* $\xi \cap \Delta$. I wish to introduce for this the briefer expression, "the T-relation *maps* the Γ-concept into the Δ-concept", by calling in general a concept whose extension is Γ, Γ-*concept*, and a relation whose extension is T, T-*relation*.

§39. Definition of the function $\mathfrak{H}\xi$.

Now if equinumeracy is to obtain between the concepts, there must be a relation concerning which there holds not only what was said above of the T-relation, but also the corresponding thing concerning its converse, where the roles of Γ and Δ are interchanged, so that it maps the Δ-concept into the Γ-concept. To this end it is desirable to introduce a function-name "$\mathaccent"7E\xi$" such that if T is the extension of a relation, $\mathaccent"7E T$ is the extension of its converse. To this end we define:

$$\vdash \grave{a}\grave{\epsilon}(a \cap (\epsilon \cap p)) = \mathaccent"7E p \qquad \text{(E}$$

The relation

$$\underline{\qquad} \xi \cap (\zeta \cap \mathaccent"7E T),$$

or

$$\underline{\qquad} \xi \cap (\zeta \cap \grave{a}\grave{\epsilon}(a \cap (\epsilon \cap T))),$$

is then the same as $\underline{\qquad} \zeta \cap (\xi \cap T)$.

§40. Definition of the function $\mathscr{B}\xi$.

Thus in order to say the same of the converse of the relation $\underline{\qquad} \xi \cap (\zeta \cap T)$ as we have said of the relation itself, we need only replace "T" by "$\mathaccent"7E T$". Accordingly, $\begin{array}{c} \text{---} \Gamma \cap (\Delta \cap) T \\ \llcorner \Delta \cap (\Gamma \cap) \mathaccent"7E T \end{array}$ is the truth-value of *the T-relation's mapping the Γ-concept into the Δ-concept, and its converse's mapping the Δ-concept into the Γ-concept*—assuming, of course, that Γ and Δ are extensions of concepts and T the extension of a relation. For these concepts to be equinumerate, there must exist such a relation. $\underline{\qquad} \xi \cap (\zeta \cap T)$ is always a relation, whatever object "T" may denote, and every relation admits of being designated in the form "$\underline{\qquad} \xi \cap (\zeta \cap T)$", by having its extension taken for T. Accordingly $\begin{array}{c} \text{---}^{\mathfrak{a}} \Gamma \cap (\Delta \cap)q \\ \llcorner \Delta \cap (\Gamma \cap) \mathaccent"7E q \end{array}$ is the truth-value of *the concepts* $\underline{\qquad} \xi \cap \Gamma$ *and* $\underline{\qquad} \xi \cap \Delta$'s *being equinumerate*. We can regard this as value of the function $\begin{array}{c} \text{---}^{\mathfrak{a}} \xi \cap (\Delta \cap)q \\ \llcorner \Delta \cap (\xi \cap) \mathaccent"7E q \end{array}$ for the argument Γ. This function is a concept, whose extension is

$$\grave{\epsilon}\left(\begin{array}{c} \text{---}^{\mathfrak{a}} \epsilon \cap (\Delta \cap)q \\ \llcorner \Delta \cap (\epsilon \cap) \mathaccent"7E q \end{array} \right).$$

And according to my definition (*Grundlagen*, §68), this extension is the *Number* that belongs to the concept $\underline{\qquad} \xi \cap \Delta$. Instead of "Number that belongs to the Δ-concept", I also say briefly, "Number of the Δ-concept". I now define:

$$\vdash \grave{\epsilon}\left(\begin{array}{c} \text{---}^{\mathfrak{a}} \epsilon \cap (u \cap)q \\ \llcorner u \cap (\epsilon \cap) \mathaccent"7E q \end{array} \right) = \mathscr{B}u \qquad \text{(Z}$$

§41. Definition of ϙ.

Accordingly, $\mathscr{B}\acute{\epsilon}(\,\rule[0.35em]{0.8em}{0.4pt}\!\!\!\!\top\, \epsilon = \epsilon)$ is the Number of the $\acute{\epsilon}(\,\rule[0.35em]{0.8em}{0.4pt}\!\!\!\!\top\, \epsilon = \epsilon)$-concept, or the Number that belongs to the concept $\rule[0.35em]{0.8em}{0.4pt}\!\!\!\!\top\, \xi = \xi$, and this is the Number nought (*Grundlagen* §74). Later it will turn out to be necessary to distinguish the Number nought from the number nought; hence I shall mark out the former by an oblique stroke. I define:

$$\Vdash \mathscr{B}\acute{\epsilon}(\,\rule[0.35em]{0.8em}{0.4pt}\!\!\!\!\top\, \epsilon = \epsilon) = \mathbf{ϙ} \tag{Θ}$$

§42. Definition of 1. Concept of Number.

In this way I also define (*Grundlagen*, §77):

$$\Vdash \mathscr{B}\acute{\epsilon}(\epsilon = \mathbf{ϙ}) = \mathbf{1} \tag{I}$$

The oblique stroke in "1" is to distinguish the Number one from the number one. Accordingly, 1 is the Number that belongs to the concept $\xi = \mathbf{ϙ}$.

$\rule[0.35em]{0.8em}{0.4pt}\!\!\!\!\top^{u}\, \mathscr{B}u = \Gamma$ is the truth-value of *there existing a concept to which the Number Γ belongs,* or as we may also say, of Γ's *being a Number.* Accordingly we call the function $\rule[0.35em]{0.8em}{0.4pt}\!\!\!\!\top^{u}\, \mathscr{B}u = \xi$ the concept of *Number.*

§43. Definition of f.

We still need to explain the relation in which a member of the Number-series stands to the member directly succeeding it. Here I cite my definition (*Grundlagen* §76) in somewhat altered wording:

If there is a concept $\rule[0.35em]{1.5em}{0.4pt}\, \xi \cap \Gamma$ and an object Δ falling under it, such that the Number belonging to the concept $\rule[0.35em]{1.5em}{0.4pt}\, \xi \cap \Gamma$ is Λ and the Number belonging to the concept $\rule[0.35em]{1em}{0.4pt}\!\!\!\top\!\!\!\rule[0em]{0pt}{0pt}_{\xi \cap \Gamma}\, \xi = \Delta$ is Θ, then I say: Λ follows in the Number-series

directly after Θ.

Now we have in

$$\rule[0em]{0pt}{0pt}\!\!\!\top\!\!\!\!\begin{array}{l} \rule[0.35em]{0.6em}{0.4pt}\mathscr{B}\Gamma = \Lambda \\ \rule[0.35em]{0.6em}{0.4pt}\Delta \cap \Gamma \\ \rule[0.35em]{0.6em}{0.4pt}\mathscr{B}\acute{\epsilon}\left(\rule[0em]{0pt}{0pt}\!\!\top\!\!\!\rule[0em]{0pt}{0pt}_{\epsilon \cap \Gamma}\, \epsilon = \Delta\right) = \Theta \end{array}$$

the truth-value of Λ's *being the Number belonging to the concept* $\rule[0.35em]{1.5em}{0.4pt}\, \xi \cap \Gamma$, *and Δ's falling under this concept, and Θ's being the number of the* $\acute{\epsilon}\left(\rule[0em]{0pt}{0pt}\!\!\top\!\!\!\rule[0em]{0pt}{0pt}_{\epsilon \cap \Gamma}\, \epsilon = \Delta\right)$*-concept.* Accordingly, we

have in

100

$$\overset{u\quad a}{\overbrace{\qquad}}\ \Vert\ \begin{array}{l} \mathscr{B}u = \Lambda \\ a \cap u \\ \mathscr{B}\acute{\epsilon}\left(\displaystyle\prod_{\epsilon \cap u} \epsilon = a\right) = \Theta \end{array}$$

the truth-value of Λ's *following in the Number-series directly after* Θ. We consider this as value of the function

$$\overset{u\quad a}{\overbrace{\qquad}}\ \Vert\ \begin{array}{l} \mathscr{B}u = \zeta \\ a \cap u \\ \mathscr{B}\acute{\epsilon}\left(\displaystyle\prod_{\epsilon \cap u} \epsilon = a\right) = \xi \end{array}$$

for the arguments Θ and Λ. The extension of this relation is

$$\grave{a}\acute{\epsilon}\left[\ \overset{u\quad a}{\overbrace{\qquad}}\ \Vert\ \begin{array}{l} \mathscr{B}u = a \\ a \cap u \\ \mathscr{B}\acute{\epsilon}\left(\displaystyle\prod_{\epsilon \cap u} \epsilon = a\right) = \epsilon \end{array}\right],$$

and for this a simpler name will be introduced:

$$\Vdash \grave{a}\acute{\epsilon}\left[\ \overset{u\quad a}{\overbrace{\qquad}}\ \Vert\ \begin{array}{l} \mathscr{B}u = a \\ a \cap u \\ \mathscr{B}\acute{\epsilon}\left(\displaystyle\prod_{\epsilon \cap u} \epsilon = a\right) = \epsilon \end{array}\right] = \mathbf{f} \tag{H}$$

Accordingly, "$\mathbf{0} \cap (\mathbf{1} \cap \mathbf{f})$" expresses that $\mathbf{1}$ follows in the Number-series directly after $\mathbf{0}$.

§44. Some propositions of Begriffsschrift as examples.

The six propositions singled out in §78 of my *Grundlagen* may be listed here in our signs*:

[1.] "$\vdash \begin{array}{l} a = \mathbf{1} \\ \mathbf{0} \cap (a \cap \mathbf{f}) \end{array}$" ,

[2.] "$\vdash \begin{array}{l} a \cap u \\ \mathscr{B}u = \mathbf{1} \end{array}$" ,

59 [3.] "$\vdash \begin{array}{l} d = a \\ a \cap u \\ d \cap u \\ \mathscr{B}u = \mathbf{1} \end{array}$" ,

[4.] "$\vdash \begin{array}{l} \mathscr{B}u = \mathbf{1} \\ e \cap u \\ a = d \\ a \cap u \\ d \cap u \end{array}$" .

------

*The corresponding assertions in words in §78 of *Grundlagen* are as follows, together with their point of appearance in the body of derived theory in *Grundgesetze*:

1. If a follows in the series of natural numbers directly after 0, then $a = 1$. [*Grundgesetze*, theorem 114.]

2. If 1 is the Number that belongs to a concept, then there exists

101

I leave it to the reader to make the sense clear to himself. "If"
expresses that the f-relation is many-one; in other words: that
for every Number, there is not more than one single Number that
follows it directly in the Number-series. "I̵f" expresses that
for every Number, there is not more than one single Number that
directly precedes it in the Number-series. The fifth of the propositions mentioned is rendered by [5.] "⊢⊤If ".
                                          ⊥I̵f

$$[6.] \quad ``⊢\underset{}{\overset{a}{\frown}}\ a\cap(a\cap f)"$$
$$⊤a = 0$$
$$\overset{u}{\frown}\ \mathscr{B}u = a$$

asserts that for every Number except 0 there is a Number immediately preceding it in the Number-series.

§45. Definition of the function $\overset{\frown}{-}\xi$. Following and preceding in a series.

The f-relation orders the Numbers in such a way that there
arises a series. We have now to explain generally the meaning
of "an object follows an object in a series", where the type of
this series is determined by the relation in which a member of
this series always stands to the member directly following. I
reiterate the explanation given in §79 of my *Grundlagen* and in
Begriffsschrift, in somewhat different words.

If the proposition

"if every object to which Δ stands in the T-relation falls

---

an object that falls under that concept. [*Grundgesetze*, theorem 113.]

3. If 1 is the Number that belongs to a concept F, then, if the object x falls under the concept F and if y falls under the concept
F, then $x = y$; that is, x is the same as y. [*Grundgesetze*, theorem 117.]

4. If an object falls under the concept F, and if it can be inferred
generally from the propositions that x falls under the concept F
and that y falls under the concept F that $x = y$, then 1 is the
Number that belongs to the concept F. [*Grundgesetze*, theorem 122.]

5. The relation of m to n that is established by the proposition:
"n follows in the series of natural numbers directly after m"
is a one-one relation. [*Grundgesetze*, theorem 90.]

6. Every Number except 0 follows in the series of natural numbers
directly after a Number. [*Grundgesetze*, theorem 107.]

under the concept ——$F(\xi)$, and if from the fact that an object falls under this concept, it follows generally that every object to which it stands in the T-relation likewise falls under the concept ——$F(\xi)$, then Θ falls under this concept"

holds good generally for every concept ——$F(\xi)$, then we say "Θ *follows in the* T-*series after* Δ".

Accordingly,

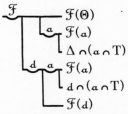

is the truth-value of Θ's *following after* Δ *in the* T-*series*. We can regard this as value of the function

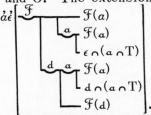

for the arguments Δ and Θ. The extension of this relation is

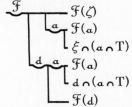

We can regard this extension as value of the function

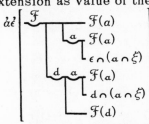

60 for the argument T. For this last function I introduce a simple name, by defining:

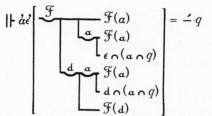

$$(K$$

Accordingly, "$\Delta \cap (\Theta \cap \overset{\cdot}{\smile} T)$" expresses that Θ follows Δ in the T-series. And "$\Delta \cap (\Theta \cap \overset{\cdot}{\smile} f)$" expresses that Θ follows Δ in the Number-series.

In place of "Θ follows Δ in the T-series", I also say, "Δ *precedes* Θ in the T-series".

§46. Definition of the function $\smile \xi$.

$\quad \overset{\Theta \,=\, \Delta}{\underset{\Delta \cap (\Theta \cap \overset{\cdot}{\smile} T)}{}}$ is the truth-value of Θ's *either following* Δ *in*

the T-*series or else coinciding with* Δ. For this I say more briefly that Θ *belongs to the* T-*series that begins with* Δ, or that Δ *belongs to the* T-*series that ends with* Θ. I regard this as value of the function $\overset{\zeta \,=\, \xi}{\underset{\xi \cap (\zeta \cap \overset{\cdot}{\smile} T)}{}}$ for the arguments Δ and Θ.

The extension of this relation is $\overset{\cdot}{a}\overset{\cdot}{\epsilon} \left(\overset{a \,=\, \epsilon}{\underset{\epsilon \cap (a \cap \overset{\cdot}{\smile} T)}{}} \right)$. This ex-

tension I regard as value of the function $\overset{\cdot}{a}\overset{\cdot}{\epsilon} \left(\overset{a \,=\, \epsilon}{\underset{\epsilon \cap (a \cap \overset{\cdot}{\smile} \xi)}{}} \right)$ for

the argument T, and I introduce a simple name, by defining:

$$\Vdash \overset{\cdot}{a}\overset{\cdot}{\epsilon} \left(\overset{a \,=\, \epsilon}{\underset{\epsilon \cap (a \cap \overset{\cdot}{\smile} q)}{}} \right) = \smile q \qquad (\Lambda$$

Accordingly, $\Delta \cap (\Theta \cap \smile T)$ is the truth-value of Θ's *belonging to the* T-*series that begins with* Δ. In virtue of which, $\mathbf{0} \cap (\Theta \cap \smile f)$ is the truth-value of Θ's *belonging to the Number-series that begins with* $\mathbf{0}$, for which I also say, that Θ is a *finite* Number.

In §82 of my *Grundlagen* I cite the proposition that the Number that belongs to the concept
belonging to the Number-series that ends with n
directly follows n in the Number-series, if n is a finite Number. We can now render this in the following way:

$$\text{"}\overset{n \cap (\mathscr{B}(n \cap \smile f) \cap f)}{\underset{\mathbf{0} \cap (n \cap \smile f)}{}}\text{"} \qquad ;$$

for $(\Theta \cap \smile f)$ is the extension of the concept *belonging to the*

104

3. DERIVED LAWS

§ 47. We have just seen how concepts and objects with which we shall be working later can be designated in our signs. But this would be of little consequence if we could not also compute with them, if we could not present trains of inference without admixture of words, could not conduct proofs. Now that we have become acquainted with the Basic Laws and the methods of inference which are to be employed, it is time to derive from them laws we shall be using later, so as to exhibit at the same time the style of calculation. First let us collect the Basic Laws and the Rules, and add a few supplementary points.

Summary of the Basic Laws

$$\begin{array}{c} a, \quad a \\ b \quad \quad a \quad \text{(I (§18)} \\ a \end{array}$$

$$f(a) \\ \quad f(a) \quad \text{(IIa (§20)}$$

$$M_\beta(f(\beta)) \\ \quad M_\beta(f(\beta)) \quad \text{(IIb (§25)}$$

$$g\left(\begin{array}{c} f(a) \\ f(b) \end{array}\right) \\ g(a = b) \quad \text{(III (§20)}$$

$$(\quad a) = (\quad b) \\ (\quad a) = (\quad b) \quad \text{(IV (§18)}$$

$$\vdash (\acute{\epsilon}f(\epsilon) = \acute{a}g(a)) = (\stackrel{a}{\smile} f(a) = g(a)) \quad \text{(V (§20)}$$

$$\vdash a = \backslash\acute{\epsilon}(a = \epsilon) \quad \text{(VI (§18)}$$

§48. Summary of the Rules.

1. *Amalgamation of horizontals.*

If as argument of the function $\quad\xi$ there occurs the value of this same function for some argument, then the horizontals may be amalgamated.

The two portions into which the horizontal stroke in "$\quad\xi$" is divided by the negation-stroke are both horizontals in our sense.

Also, the lower horizontal stroke and the two parts of the upper horizontal stroke in "$\displaystyle\mathop{\rule{0pt}{0pt}}_{\zeta}^{\xi}$" are all horizontals in our sense.

Finally, the strokes directly on either side of the concavity in "$\overset{a}{\smile}\,\phi(a)$" are horizontals in our sense.

2. *Interchange of subcomponents*.

The subcomponents of the same proposition may be interchanged with one another as desired.

3. *Contraposition*.

A subcomponent may be interchanged in a proposition with the main component if the truth-value of each is simultaneously reversed.

Transition-sign: ✕.

4. *Amalgamation of identical subcomponents*.

A subcomponent occurring more than once in the same proposition need be written only once.

5. *Conversion of a Roman letter to a Gothic letter.*   62

A Roman letter may be replaced at all of its occurrences in a proposition by one and the same Gothic letter, viz., an object-letter by an object-letter, and a function-letter by a function-letter. The Gothic letter must then at the same time be inserted over a concavity in front of a main component outside which the Roman letter did not occur. If within this main component is contained the scope of a Gothic letter, and within this scope the Roman letter occurs, then the Gothic letter replacing this Roman letter must be different from the Gothic letter already present.

Transition-sign: ⌣ .

This sign is also used if several Gothic letters are to be introduced in this way. Although one may write the end result directly, the Gothic letters must be understood as introduced one after the other.

6. *Inference (a)*.

If a subcomponent of a proposition differs from another proposition only in lacking the judgment-stroke, then a proposition may be inferred that results from the first proposition by suppressing that subcomponent.

106

Transition-signs: ( ):──────

and

( )::────── ;

combined inferences: (,):: ═══ .

7. *Inference (b).*

If the same combination of signs (proper name or Roman object-mark) appears in one proposition as main component and in another as subcomponent, a proposition may be inferred in which the main component of the second is main component, and all subcomponents of either, save the one mentioned, are subcomponents. Here, by Rule (4), identical subcomponents may be amalgamated.

Transition-signs: ( ):─ ─ ─

and

( )::─ ─ ─ ;

combined inferences: (,):: ═ ═ ═ ═

and

(,):: ═════ .

8. *Inference (c).*

If two propositions agree in their main components, while a subcomponent of one differs from a subcomponent of the other only in a negation-stroke's being prefixed, then a proposition may be inferred in which the common main component is main component, and all subcomponents of either, save the two mentioned, are subcomponents.

Transition-sign: ( ): ·─·─·─·─· .

9. *Citation of propositions. Replacement of Roman letters.*

Where a proposition is cited by its index, a simple inference may be incorporated in which every Roman object-letter is replaced at all of its occurrences in the proposition by the same proper name or the same Roman object-mark.

Likewise, each of the Roman function-letters *"f"*, *"g"*, *"h"*, *"F"*, *"G"*, *"H"* may be replaced at all of its occurrences in the proposition by the same name or the same Roman mark of a first-level function of one or two arguments, according as the Roman function-letter indicates a function of one or two arguments.

Where the Law (IIb) is cited, *"M_β"* may be replaced at both of its occurrences by the same name or the same Roman mark of a second-level function of one argument of type 2.

Regarding the word "same" in the second and third paragraphs of this Rule, it is to be observed that the argument is not a part of the function, and that hence a change of argument-sign does not alter the function-name. If the same function-name is to occur at more than one point, it is necessary that the related argument-places correspond with each other. As to the question of which are to be regarded as related argument-places, these rules are to be observed:

All places at which there occurs a Gothic letter within its scope, yet not within an enclosed scope of the same letter and not over a concavity, are related argument-places of the corresponding function.

All places at which there occurs a small Greek vowel within its scope, yet not within an enclosed scope of the same letter and not with a smooth breathing, are related argument-places of the corresponding function.

10. *Citation of propositions. Change of Gothic letter.*

Where a proposition is cited by its index, a Gothic letter may be replaced over the concavity and at all argument-places of the corresponding function by another Gothic letter, viz., an object-letter by an object-letter and a function-letter by a function-letter, the same throughout: so long as this does not result in a Gothic letter, occurring in a scope enclosed within its own, becoming the same as the letter already present whose scope is the one enclosed.

11. *Citation of propositions. Change of Greek vowel.*

Where a proposition is cited by its index, a Greek vowel may be replaced under the smooth breathing and at all argument-places of the corresponding function by another Greek vowel, the same throughout: so long as this does not result in a Greek letter, occurring in a scope enclosed within its own, becoming the same as the letter already present whose scope is the one enclosed.

12. *Citation of definitions.*

Where a definition is cited by its index, the definition-stroke may be replaced by the judgment-stroke, and any alterations 6 made that are permitted by Rules (9), (10), and (11) for the citation of propositions.

108

13. The entire context standing to the right of a horizontal is to be regarded as a whole s t a n d i n g in the place of "ξ" in "$\underline{\quad}\,\xi$", except as brackets prohibit this.

14. The entire context standing to the left of the identity-sign as far as (but not including) the nearest horizontal is to be regarded as a whole standing in the place of "ξ" in "$\xi = \zeta$", except as brackets prohibit this.

Accordingly "$a = b = c$", for example, is to be regarded as "$(a = b) = c$". But since "$a = b = c$" can also be used in another sense, I shall in that case insert the brackets.

15. Everything standing to the right of an identity-sign as far as (but not including) the nearest identity-sign is to be regarded as a whole standing in the place of "ζ" in "$\xi = \zeta$", except as brackets prohibit this.

16. We have certain names of functions of two arguments, such as "$\xi = \zeta$" and "$\xi \cap \zeta$", possessing argument-places on the left-hand and on the right-hand side. Such function-signs I shall call *bilateral*. For bilateral function-signs, with the exception of the identity-sign, let the following hold:

The entire context standing to the left of such a sign as far as the nearest identity-sign or horizontal is to be regarded as a whole standing at the left-hand argument-place, except as brackets prohibit this; and the entire context standing to the right of such a sign as far as the nearest bilateral function-sign is to be regarded as a whole standing at the right-hand argument-place, except as brackets prohibit this.

17. Names of functions of one argument have hitherto been, and in the sequel will be, so formed that the argument-place stands to the right of the function-sign proper, as with "$I\xi$", "$)\xi$", "$\maltese\xi$", "$\mathfrak{a}\xi$", "$\underline{}\xi$", "$\backsim\xi$". For such *unilateral* function-signs, with the exception of the horizontal, let the following hold:

The entire context standing to the right of a unilateral function-sign as far as the nearest bilateral function-sign is to be regarded as a whole standing at the argument-place of the unilateral function-sign.

18. If a horizontal terminates at the left unattached, then we enclose it together with its argument-sign in brackets.

§49. Derivation of some propositions from (I).

Let us first derive some propositions from (I).

I shall now cite (I) in this way: by Rule (9) of §48 I write "$\!-b$" for "b", and by Rule (1) I amalgamate the horizontals. My way of citing a proposition is shown by the following:

$$\text{I} \quad \begin{array}{l} \vdash a \\ \;\; b \\ \;\; a \end{array}$$

$$\times$$

$$\begin{array}{l} \vdash b \\ \;\; a \\ \;\; a \end{array} \tag{Ia}$$

By the above, "(Ia)" is made the index of the new proposition. As for the transition, compare Rule (3). Use is also made of the interchangeability of subcomponents by Rule (2).

In the following derivation I cite (I) by writing "$\!-a$" for "a".

$$\text{I} \quad \begin{array}{l} \vdash a \\ \;\; b \\ \;\; a \end{array}$$

$$\times$$

$$\begin{array}{l} \vdash a \\ \;\; a \\ \;\; b \end{array} \tag{Ib}$$

Here in applying Rule (3) "$\begin{smallmatrix} a \\ b \end{smallmatrix}$" is to be regarded as the main component.

$$\text{I} \quad \begin{array}{l} \vdash a \\ \;\; b \\ \;\; a \end{array} \qquad\qquad \text{Ia} \quad \begin{array}{l} \vdash b \\ \;\; a \\ \;\; a \end{array}$$

$$\times \qquad\qquad\qquad\qquad \times$$

$$\begin{array}{l} \vdash a \\ \;\; a \\ \;\; b \end{array} \tag{Ic} \qquad\qquad \begin{array}{l} \vdash a \\ \;\; b \\ \;\; a \end{array} \tag{Id}$$

In the following derivation, (I) is understood in the form "$\vdash \begin{smallmatrix} a \\ a \end{smallmatrix}$", and now "$\begin{smallmatrix} a \\ b \end{smallmatrix}$" is written in place of "a". (If we assume (I) in the original form and write "$\begin{smallmatrix} a \\ b \end{smallmatrix}$" instead of "$a$", then we first obtain

110

"

in which we can amalgamate the identical subcomponents by Rule (4). We can also regard the following in the same way.)

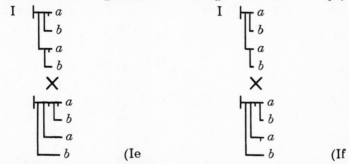

I ... (Ie

I ... (If

We may compare with this the remarks in §12 concerning "and".

In the following (Ie) is cited by our writing "a" for "b" and amalgamating the identical subcomponents.

Ie

(Ig

§50. Derivation of the main principles of the function $\xi = \zeta$.

Now we shall derive the chief laws governing the function $\xi = \zeta$. For a start, by Rule (9) of §48 we replace the function-letter "g" in (III) by our name of the function —— ξ and amalgamate the horizontals.

III
$\ell(a)$
$\ell(b)$
$a = b$

(IIb): ― ― ― ― ―

$f(a)$
$f(b)$
$a = b$

(IIIa

66

111

This transition is made by Rule (7), and (IIb) is cited in the form

$$``\begin{array}{l} \vdash \!\! \begin{array}{l} f(a) \\ f(b) \end{array} \\ \quad\ell\, \begin{array}{l} \mathfrak{f}(a) \\ \mathfrak{f}(b) \end{array} \end{array}"\ ,$$

where by Rule (9) "$\mathrm{M}_{\beta}(\phi(\beta))$" is replaced by the Roman mark of a second-level function "$\begin{array}{l}\phi(a)\\\phi(b)\end{array}$".

$$\text{IIIa}\quad \begin{array}{l} \vdash\!\!\begin{array}{l} f(a) \\ f(b) \end{array} \\ \quad a = b \end{array}$$

$$\times$$

$$\begin{array}{l} \vdash\!\!\begin{array}{l} a = b \\ f(b) \end{array} \\ \quad f(a) \end{array} \qquad\qquad\qquad\text{(IIIb}$$

In the following derivation the function-letter "f" in (IIIa) is replaced by the Roman function-mark "$\!\!\!-\!\!f(\xi)$", and the horizontals are amalgamated.

$$\text{IIIa}\quad \begin{array}{l} \vdash\!\!\begin{array}{l} f(a) \\ f(b) \end{array} \\ \quad a = b \end{array}$$

$$\times$$

$$\begin{array}{l} \vdash\!\!\begin{array}{l} f(b) \\ f(a) \end{array} \\ \quad a = b \end{array} \qquad\qquad\qquad\text{(IIIc}$$

$$\times$$

$$\begin{array}{l} \vdash\!\!\begin{array}{l} a = b \\ f(a) \end{array} \\ \quad f(b) \end{array} \qquad\qquad\qquad\text{(IIId}$$

We may render (IIIa) in words somewhat as follows: if a coincides with b, then everything that holds of b holds of a. (IIIc) is similar. (IIId) we may express thus: if a statement holds for a that does not hold for b, then a does not coincide with b.

In the following derivation the function-letter "g" in (III) is replaced by the function-name "$\!\!\!-\!\!\xi$" and "b" is replaced by "a".

$$\text{III} \quad \begin{array}{l} \ell \quad f(a) \\ \quad f(a) \\ \quad a = a \end{array}$$

$$\times$$

$$\begin{array}{l} a = a \\ \ell \quad f(a) \\ \quad f(a) \end{array} \qquad (a$$

— • —

$$\text{I} \quad \begin{array}{l} f(a) \\ f(a) \end{array}$$

$$\begin{array}{l} \ell \quad f(a) \\ \quad f(a) \end{array} \qquad (\beta$$

$$(a){:} \; \underline{\qquad\qquad}$$

$$\vdash a = a \qquad (\text{IIIe}$$

This last proposition is indeed obvious by our explanation of the identity-sign, but it is worthwhile to see the way in which it can be developed out of (III). Furthermore this gives us an opportunity to note some points that are also to hold for later derivations. The second proposition has been given the index "a". A small Greek letter used in this way is to retain a fixed meaning as an index only within a given derivation, so that in another derivation it may be used as index for a different proposition. A derivation terminates with a proposition that first receives an index other than a small Greek letter. In our derivation above there follows beneath the proposition (a) the sign

"— • —",

to announce that we are there breaking off the train of inference and initiating a new one, which is only linked to the earlier at the point at which we cite (a). The transition to (β) follows by Rule (5), and that from (β) to (IIIe) by Rule (6). Now let us, in (IIIa), replace the function-letter "f" by the Roman function-mark "$b = \xi$".

$$\text{IIIa} \quad \begin{array}{l} b = a \\ b = b \\ a = b \end{array}$$

$$(\text{IIIe}){::} \; \underline{\qquad\qquad}$$

$$\begin{array}{l} b = a \\ a = b \end{array} \qquad (\text{IIIf}$$

This inference follows by Rule (6).

In the following inference, in (IIIc) and (IIIa) "a" is replaced by "$——a$", "b" by "$—_{\top}a$", and the function-letter "f" by the function-name "$——\xi$", and the horizontals are amalgamated where possible.

$$\text{IIIc} \quad \begin{array}{l} \rule{0pt}{0pt} \!\!\vdash\!\!\top a \\ \qquad\!\!\llcorner a \\ \qquad\llcorner (——a) = (—_{\top}a) \end{array}$$

$$\times$$

$$\begin{array}{l} \vdash\!\!\top (——a) = (—_{\top}a) \\ \quad \llcorner a \end{array} \qquad\qquad (a$$

$$——\bullet——$$

$$\text{IIIa} \quad \begin{array}{l} \vdash\!\!\top a \\ \qquad\!\!\llcorner_{\top} a \\ \qquad\llcorner (——a) = (—_{\top}a) \end{array}$$

$$\times$$

$$\begin{array}{l} \vdash\!\!\top (——a) = (—_{\top}a) \\ \quad \llcorner_{\top} a \end{array} \qquad\qquad (\beta$$

$$(a): \cdot—\cdot—\cdot—\cdot—\cdot—\cdot$$
$$\vdash (——a) = (—_{\top}a) \qquad\qquad (\text{IIIg}$$

In the transitions to (a) and (β) the identical subcomponents are amalgamated by Rule (4). The last inference is made by Rule (8).

In the following derivation we replace the function-letter "f" in (IIIc) by the Roman function-mark "$f(a) = f(\xi)$".

$$\text{IIIc} \quad \begin{array}{l} \vdash\!\!\top f(a) = f(b) \\ \qquad\!\!\llcorner f(a) = f(a) \\ \qquad\llcorner a = b \end{array}$$

$$(\text{IIIe}):: ————————$$

$$\begin{array}{l} \vdash\!\!\top f(a) = f(b) \\ \quad \llcorner a = b \end{array} \qquad\qquad (\text{IIIh}$$

In the following derivation the function-letter "g" in (III) is replaced by "$—_{\top} F(——\xi)$" and the horizontals are amalgamated.

III $\quad$

$$\vdash_{\top} F\!\left(\underset{\ell}{\smile_{\top}} \begin{matrix} \ell(a) \\ \ell(b) \end{matrix}\right)$$
$$\vdash_{\top} F(\underline{\quad} a = b$$

$$\times$$

$$\vdash_{\top} F(\underline{\quad} a = b)$$
$$\vdash_{\top} F\!\left(\underset{\ell}{\smile_{\top}} \begin{matrix} \ell(a) \\ \ell(b) \end{matrix}\right)$$

$\qquad\qquad\qquad\qquad\qquad$ $(\alpha$

(III):: $----$

$$\vdash_{\top} F(\underline{\quad} a = b)$$
$$\vdash F(a = b)$$

$\qquad\qquad\qquad\qquad\qquad$ $(\beta$

$$\vdash_{\top}\ell(\underline{\quad} a = b)$$
$$\vdash \ell(a = b)$$

$\qquad\qquad\qquad\qquad\qquad$ $(\gamma$

$$\underline{\quad} \bullet \underline{\quad}$$

III $\quad$

$$\vdash_{\top}\ell(\underline{\quad} a = b)$$
$$\vdash \ell(a = b)$$
$$\vdash_{\top}(\underline{\quad} a = b) = (a = b)$$

$$\times$$

$$\vdash_{\top}(\underline{\quad} a = b) = (a = b)$$
$$\vdash_{\ell}\ell(\underline{\quad} a = b)$$
$$\vdash \ell(a = b)$$

$\qquad\qquad\qquad\qquad\qquad$ $(\delta$

$(\gamma)::$ $\overline{\qquad\qquad\qquad\qquad\qquad}$

$$\vdash (\underline{\quad} a = b) = (a = b)$$

$\qquad\qquad\qquad\qquad\qquad$ (IIIi

In the second citation of (III) "g" is replaced by "F". In the last citation of (III), "$g(\xi)$" is replaced by "$\top\, \xi$", "a" by "$\underline{\quad} a = b$", and "b" by "$a = b$".

§51. Derivation of some propositions from (IV).

Now some propositions will be derived from (IV).

IIIa $\quad$

$$\vdash_{\top} a$$
$$\vdash_{\top} b$$
$$\vdash (\underline{\quad} a) = (\top\, b)$$

$$\times$$

$$\vdash_{\top}(\underline{\quad} a) = (\top\, b)$$
$$\vdash_{\top} a$$
$$\vdash b$$

$\qquad\qquad\qquad\qquad\qquad$ $(\alpha$

$$\underline{\quad} \bullet \underline{\quad}$$

115

IIIc
$$b$$
$$a$$
$$(\underline{\quad} a) = (\underline{\quad} b)$$

$$\times$$

$$(\underline{\quad} a) = (\underline{\quad} b)$$
$$b$$
$$a$$

(β

(I):: − − − − − −

$$(\underline{\quad} a) = (\underline{\quad} b)$$
$$b$$
$$a$$
$$a$$

(γ

(I):: − − − − − −

$$(\underline{\quad} a) = (\underline{\quad} b)$$
$$b$$
$$a$$
$$a$$
$$b$$
$$b$$

(δ

$$\underline{\quad} \bullet \underline{\quad}$$

β $$(\underline{\quad} a) = (\underline{\quad} b)$$
$$b$$
$$a$$

(I):: − − − − − −

$$(\underline{\quad} a) = (\underline{\quad} b)$$
$$b$$
$$a$$
$$b$$

(ε

(δ): ·−·−·−·−·

$$(\underline{\quad} a) = (\underline{\quad} b)$$
$$a$$
$$b$$
$$b$$
$$a$$
$$a$$
$$b$$

(ζ

(a): ·−·−·−·−·

116

$$\vdash \begin{array}{l} (\text{---} a) = (\text{---} b) \\ \quad a \\ \quad b \\ \quad b \\ \quad a \end{array}$$

$(\eta$

(IV): $- - - - - - - -$

$$\vdash \begin{array}{l} (\text{---} a) = (\text{---} b) \\ \quad b \\ \quad a \\ \quad a \\ \quad b \end{array}$$

(IVa

(I) is to be understood in its first application above in the form

$$\text{``} \begin{array}{l} b \\ a \\ b \\ a \end{array} \text{''} \quad ,$$

in its second application, in the form

$$\text{``} \begin{array}{l} a \\ b \\ a \\ b \end{array} \text{''} \quad ,$$

and in its third application, in the form

$$\text{``} \begin{array}{l} a \\ b \\ a \\ b \end{array} \text{''} \quad .$$

Note the effect of this use of (I) upon the transitions to (γ), (δ), and (ϵ). (I) will frequently be used again in this way. We may compare the derivation of (Ie) in §49. The proposition (IVa) is frequently used to prove the identity of truth-values.

IV $\begin{array}{l} (\text{---} a) = (\text{--}\tau\text{ } a) \\ (\text{---} a) = (\text{--}\tau\tau\text{ } a) \end{array}$

$$\times$$

$\begin{array}{l} (\text{---} a) = (\text{--}\tau\tau\text{ } a) \\ (\text{---} a) = (\text{--}\tau\text{ } a) \end{array}$

(IIIg):: $\overline{}$

$\vdash (\text{---} a) = (\text{--}\tau\tau\text{ } a)$

(IVb

(IIIa): $\overline{}$

117

$$\left. \begin{array}{l} \vdash f(\text{——} a) \\ f(\text{——} a) \end{array} \right.$$ (IVc

$$\text{——}\bullet\text{——}$$

$$\begin{array}{l} \text{IVb} \quad \vdash (\text{——} a) = (\text{——} a) \\ \text{(IIIc):} \rule{4cm}{0.4pt} \end{array}$$

$$\left. \begin{array}{l} \vdash f(\text{——} a) \\ f(\text{——} a) \end{array} \right.$$ (IVd

A sample of the application of (IVa) is the following.

$$\text{IIIf} \quad \left[\begin{array}{l} a = b \\ b = a \end{array} \right.$$

$$\text{(IVa):} \rule{2cm}{0.4pt}$$

$$\left[\begin{array}{l} (\text{——} a = b) = (\text{——} b = a) \\ b = a \\ a = b \end{array} \right.$$ $(a$

$$\text{(IIIf)::} \rule{6cm}{0.4pt}$$

$$\vdash (\text{——} a = b) = (\text{——} b = a)$$ $(\beta$

$$\text{(IIIc):} \rule{5cm}{0.4pt}$$

$$\left[\begin{array}{l} (a = b) = (\text{——} b = a) \\ (\text{——} a = b) = (a = b) \end{array} \right.$$ $(\gamma$

$$\text{(IIIi)::} \rule{5cm}{0.4pt}$$

$$\vdash (a = b) = (\text{——} b = a)$$ $(\delta$

$$\text{(IIIc):} \rule{5cm}{0.4pt}$$

$$\left[\begin{array}{l} (a = b) = (b = a) \\ (\text{——} b = a) = (b = a) \end{array} \right.$$ $(\epsilon$

$$\text{(IIIi)::} \rule{5cm}{0.4pt}$$

$$\vdash (a = b) = (b = a)$$ (IVe

In the transition to (γ) above, (IIIc) is to be understood in the form

$$\text{``} \left[\begin{array}{l} (a = b) = (\text{——} b = a) \\ (\text{——} a = b) = (\text{——} b = a) \\ (\text{——} a = b) = (a = b) \end{array} \right. \text{''}$$

where   "$f(\xi)$"   is replaced by   "$\xi = (\text{——} b = a)$",

         "a"   is replaced by   "$(\text{——} a = b)$",

and   "b"   is replaced by   "$(a = b)$".

For the transition to (ϵ), we are to think of

       "$f(\xi)$"   in (IIIc) as replaced by   "$(a = b) = \xi$",

        "a"   as replaced by   "$(\text{——} b = a)$",

and   "b"   as replaced by   "$(b = a)$".

§52. Derivation of some propositions from (V) and (VI).

Finally, some further propositions may be derived from (V) and (VI).

$$\text{V} \quad \vdash (\acute{\epsilon}f(\epsilon) = \acute{\alpha}g(\alpha)) = (\overset{a}{\smile}f(a) = g(a))$$

(IIIa): ──────────────────

$$\vdash\!\!\!\!\begin{array}{l} \acute{\epsilon}f(\epsilon) = \acute{\alpha}g(a) \\ \overset{a}{\smile} f(a) = g(a) \end{array}$$

(IIIh): ─ ─ ─ ─ ─ ─ ─ ─

$$\vdash\!\!\!\!\begin{array}{l} F(\acute{\epsilon}f(\epsilon)) = F(\acute{\alpha}g(a)) \\ \overset{a}{\smile} f(a) = g(a) \end{array}$$
(Va

── • ──

$$\text{V} \quad \vdash (\acute{\epsilon}f(\epsilon) = \acute{\alpha}g(a)) = (\overset{a}{\smile}f(a) = g(a))$$

(IIIc): ──────────────────

$$\vdash\!\!\!\!\begin{array}{l} \overset{a}{\smile} f(a) = g(a) \\ \acute{\epsilon}f(\epsilon) = \acute{\alpha}g(a) \end{array}$$
(a

(IIa): ─ ─ ─ ─ ─ ─ ─ ─

$$\vdash\!\!\!\!\begin{array}{l} f(a) = g(a) \\ \acute{\epsilon}f(\epsilon) = \acute{\alpha}g(a) \end{array}$$
(Vb

In (IIa) as cited here, "$f(\xi)$" is to be thought of as replaced by "$f(\xi) = g(\xi)$".

In the following derivation "$g(\xi)$" in (Va) is r e p l a c e d by "$a = \xi$", and "ϵ" is written for "a" in accordance with Rule (11) of §48.

$$\text{Va} \quad \vdash\!\!\!\!\begin{array}{l} \acute{\epsilon}f(\epsilon) = \acute{\epsilon}(a = \epsilon) \\ \overset{a}{\smile} f(a) = (a = a) \end{array}$$

(IIIa): ─ ─ ─ ─ ─ ─ ─ ─

$$\vdash\!\!\!\!\begin{array}{l} a = \backslash\acute{\epsilon}f(\epsilon) \\ a = \backslash\acute{\epsilon}(a = \epsilon) \\ \overset{a}{\smile} f(a) = (a = a) \end{array}$$
(a

(VI): ──────────────────

$$\vdash\!\!\!\!\begin{array}{l} a = \backslash\acute{\epsilon}f(\epsilon) \\ \overset{a}{\smile} f(a) = (a = a) \end{array}$$
(VIa

119

APPENDICES

APPENDIX I

DERIVATION OF "$\vdash f(a) = a \cap \acute{\epsilon} f(\epsilon)$"
(*Grundgesetze*, Vol. I, §§54, 55, 91)

§54. Analysis.

73   ... the proposition

$$\text{``}\vdash f(a) = a \cap \acute{\epsilon} f(\epsilon)\text{''} \tag{1}$$

is to be derived by way of Definition (A) [of §34]. According to that, it is sufficient to prove

$$\text{``}\vdash f(a) = \backslash \grave{a} \left(\begin{array}{c} \text{—}\!\!\text{—} \mathfrak{a}(a) = a \\ \grave{\epsilon} f(\epsilon) = \grave{\epsilon} \mathfrak{a}(\epsilon) \end{array} \right)\text{''} . \tag{λ}$$

This must be done by means of (VIa) and the proposition

$$\text{``}\vdash\!\!\!\!\begin{array}{c} a \\ \end{array}\!\!\left(\begin{array}{c} \text{—}\!\!\text{—} \mathfrak{a}(a) = a \\ \grave{\epsilon} f(\epsilon) = \grave{\epsilon} \mathfrak{a}(\epsilon) \end{array} \right) = (f(a) = a)\text{''} , \tag{κ}$$

by taking for "$f(\xi)$" in (VIa)

$$\text{``} \begin{array}{c} \text{—}\!\!\text{—} \mathfrak{a}(a) = \xi \\ \grave{\epsilon} f(\epsilon) = \grave{\epsilon} \mathfrak{a}(\epsilon) \end{array}\text{''}$$

and replacing "a" by "$f(a)$". By Rule (5), (κ) results from

$$\text{``}\vdash \left(\begin{array}{c} \text{—}\!\!\text{—} \mathfrak{a}(a) = b \\ \grave{\epsilon} f(\epsilon) = \grave{\epsilon} \mathfrak{a}(\epsilon) \end{array} \right) = (f(a) = b)\text{''} , \tag{η}$$

which is proved by means of (IVa). To this end we need the propositions

$$\text{``}\begin{array}{c} \mathfrak{a}(a) = b \\ \grave{\epsilon} f(\epsilon) = \grave{\epsilon} \mathfrak{a}(\epsilon) \\ f(a) = b \end{array}\text{''} \tag{ζ}$$

and

$$\text{``}\begin{array}{c} f(a) = b \\ \mathfrak{a}(a) = b \\ \grave{\epsilon} f(\epsilon) = \grave{\epsilon} \mathfrak{a}(\epsilon) \end{array}\text{''} , \tag{γ}$$

the first of which follows by contraposition (Rule (3)) from

$$\text{``}\begin{array}{c} f(a) = b \\ \mathfrak{a}(a) = b \\ \grave{\epsilon} f(\epsilon) = \grave{\epsilon} \mathfrak{a}(\epsilon) \end{array}\text{''} . \tag{ϵ}$$

123

If we now write (IIb) in the form

$$``\vdash \begin{array}{l} f(a) = b \\ \acute{\epsilon} f(\epsilon) = \acute{\epsilon} f(\epsilon) \\ g(a) = b \\ \acute{\epsilon} f(\epsilon) = \acute{\epsilon} g(\epsilon) \end{array} \text{''} ,$$

we see that from it and (IIIe), (ϵ) follows. The second proposition (γ) follows by contraposition from

$$``\vdash \begin{array}{l} g(a) = b \\ \acute{\epsilon} f(\epsilon) = \acute{\epsilon} g(\epsilon) \\ f(a) = b \end{array} \text{''} , \qquad (\beta$$

and this by Rule (5) from

$$``\vdash \begin{array}{l} g(a) = b \\ \acute{\epsilon} f(\epsilon) = \acute{\epsilon} g(\epsilon) \\ f(a) = b \end{array} \text{''} . \qquad (\alpha$$

The latter proposition results by Rule (7) and (Vb) from

$$``\vdash \begin{array}{l} g(a) = b \\ f(a) = g(a) \\ f(a) = b \end{array} \text{''} ,$$

which with interchange of subcomponents is merely a special case of (IIIc). From this starting point we now construct the proof. ...

§55. Construction.

74

$$\text{Vb} \quad \vdash \begin{array}{l} f(a) = g(a) \\ \acute{\epsilon} f(\epsilon) = \acute{\epsilon} g(\epsilon) \end{array}$$

(IIIc): $- - - - - - -$

$$\vdash \begin{array}{l} g(a) = b \\ \acute{\epsilon} f(\epsilon) = \acute{\epsilon} g(\epsilon) \\ f(a) = b \end{array} \qquad (\alpha$$

$$\vdash \begin{array}{l} g(a) = b \\ \acute{\epsilon} f(\epsilon) = \acute{\epsilon} g(\epsilon) \\ f(a) = b \end{array} \qquad (\beta$$

$$\times$$

$$\vdash \begin{array}{l} f(a) = b \\ g(a) = b \\ \acute{\epsilon} f(\epsilon) = \acute{\epsilon} g(\epsilon) \end{array} \qquad (\gamma$$

(IVa): $\underline{\hspace{4cm}}$

124

$$\vdash \left(\begin{array}{l} \neg\mathcal{g} \!\!-\!\! q(a) = b \\ \;\dot\epsilon f(\epsilon) = \dot\epsilon\, q(\epsilon) \end{array} \right) = (\text{---}\, f(a) = b)$$
$$\vdash\!\!\!-\!\!\mathcal{g}\!\!-\!\! q(a) = b$$
$$\;\dot\epsilon f(\epsilon) = \dot\epsilon\, q(\epsilon)$$
$$\text{---}\, f(a) = b \qquad\qquad (\delta$$

— • —

IIIe $\quad \vdash \dot\epsilon f(\epsilon) = \dot\epsilon f(\epsilon)$

(IIb): $\rule{6cm}{0.4pt}$

$$\vdash\!\!\!-\!\!-\!\! f(a) = b$$
$$\!\!\!-\mathcal{g}\!\!-\!\! q(a) = b$$
$$\dot\epsilon f(\epsilon) = \dot\epsilon\, q(\epsilon) \qquad\qquad (\epsilon$$

$$\times$$

$$\vdash\!\!\!-\!\!\mathcal{g}\!\!-\!\! q(a) = b$$
$$\dot\epsilon f(\epsilon) = \dot\epsilon\, q(\epsilon)$$
$$\text{---}\, f(a) = b \qquad\qquad (\zeta$$

(δ): $\rule{6cm}{0.4pt}$

$$\vdash \left(\begin{array}{l} \neg\mathcal{g}\!\!-\!\! q(a) = b \\ \dot\epsilon f(\epsilon) = \dot\epsilon\, q(\epsilon) \end{array} \right) = (\text{---}\, f(a) = b) \qquad (\eta$$

(IIIa): $\rule{8cm}{0.4pt}$

$$\vdash \left(\begin{array}{l} \neg\mathcal{g}\!\!-\!\! q(a) = b \\ \dot\epsilon f(\epsilon) = \dot\epsilon\, q(\epsilon) \end{array} \right) = (\text{---}\, f(a) = b)$$
$$(\text{---}\, f(a) = b) = (f(a) = b) \qquad (\theta$$

(IIIi):: $\rule{8cm}{0.4pt}$

$$\vdash \left(\begin{array}{l} \neg\mathcal{g}\!\!-\!\! q(a) = b \\ \dot\epsilon f(\epsilon) = \dot\epsilon\, q(\epsilon) \end{array} \right) = (f(a) = b) \qquad (\iota$$

$$\vdash\!\!\sqsupset\!\! a \left(\begin{array}{l} \neg\mathcal{g}\!\!-\!\! q(a) = a \\ \dot\epsilon f(\epsilon) = \dot\epsilon\, q(\epsilon) \end{array} \right) = (f(a) = a) \qquad (\kappa$$

(VIa): $\rule{7cm}{0.4pt}$

$$\vdash f(a) = \backslash\dot a \left(\neg\mathcal{g}\!\!-\!\! q(a) = a \atop \dot\epsilon f(\epsilon) = \dot\epsilon\, q(\epsilon) \right) \qquad (\lambda$$

(IIIa): $\rule{6cm}{0.4pt}$

$$\vdash f(a) = a \cap \dot\epsilon f(\epsilon)$$
$$\backslash\dot a \left(\neg\mathcal{g}\!\!-\!\! q(a) = a \atop \dot\epsilon f(\epsilon) = \dot\epsilon\, q(\epsilon) \right) = a \cap \dot\epsilon f(\epsilon) \qquad (\mu$$

(A):: $\rule{6cm}{0.4pt}$

$$\vdash f(a) = a \cap \dot\epsilon f(\epsilon) \qquad (1$$

— • —

§91.

$$\text{(IIIc): } \dfrac{1 \quad \vdash f(a) = a \cap \grave{\epsilon} f(\epsilon)}{\begin{array}{l} \vdash F(a \cap \grave{\epsilon} f(\epsilon)) \\ \quad F(f(a)) \end{array}}$$

117

(77

— • —

$$\text{(IIIa): } \dfrac{1 \quad \vdash f(a) = a \cap \grave{\epsilon} f(\epsilon)}{\begin{array}{l} \vdash F(f(a)) \\ \quad F(a \cap \grave{\epsilon} f(\epsilon)) \end{array}}$$

120

(82

— • —

APPENDIX II

THE RUSSELL PARADOX
(*Grundgesetze*, Vol. II, Appendix)

53 Hardly anything more unwelcome can befall a scientific writer than that one of the foundations of his edifice be shaken after the work is finished.

I have been placed in this position by a letter of Mr. Bertrand Russell just as the printing of this [second] volume was nearing completion. It is a matter of my Basic Law (V). I have never concealed from myself its lack of the self-evidence which the others possess, and which must properly be demanded of a law of logic, and in fact I pointed out this weakness in the Introduction to the first volume (pp. 3-4, above). I should gladly have relinquished this foundation if I had known of any substitute for it. And even now I do not see how arithmetic can be scientifically founded, how numbers can be conceived as logical objects and brought under study, unless we are allowed—at least conditionally—the transition from a concept to its extension. Is it always permissible to speak of the extension of a concept, of a class? And if not, how do we recognize the exceptional cases? Can we always infer from the extension of one concept's coinciding with that of a second, that every object which falls under the first concept also falls under the second? These are the questions raised by Mr. Russell's communication.

Solatium miseris, socios habuisse malorum. I too have this solace, if solace it is; for everyone who in his proofs has made use of extensions of concepts, classes, sets,[1] is in the same position. It is not just a matter of my particular method of laying the foundations, but of whether a logical foundation for arithmetic is possible at all.

But let us come to the point. Mr. Russell has discovered a

---

[1]Herr R. Dedekind's 'systems' also come under this head.

contradiction, which may now be set out.

No one will want to assert of the class of men that it is a man. Here we have a class that does not belong to itself. That is, I say that something belongs to a class if it falls under the concept whose extension that class is. Now let us fix our attention upon the concept *class that does not belong to itself*. The extension of this concept (if we may speak of its extension) is accordingly the class of classes that do not belong to themselves. For short we shall call it the class C. Now let us ask whether this class C belongs to itself. First let us suppose that it does. If something belongs to a class, then it falls under the concept whose extension the class is; accordingly if our class C belongs to itself then it is a class that does not belong to itself. Thus our first supposition leads to a self-contradiction. Second, let us suppose that our class C does not belong to itself; then it falls under the concept whose extension it itself is, and thus does belong to itself: here again, a contradiction.

What should be our attitude to this? Are we to suppose that the law of excluded middle does not hold for classes? Or are we to suppose that there are cases in which to an unexceptionable concept no class corresponds as its extension? In the first case we should find ourselves obliged to deny that classes are objects in the full sense; for if classes were proper objects the law of excluded middle would have to hold for them. On the other hand there is nothing 'unsaturated', nothing 'predicative', about classes that would characterize them as functions, concepts, or relations. What we are accustomed to regard as a name of a class, e.g., "the class of prime numbers", has rather the nature of a proper name; it cannot occur predicatively, but it can occur as grammatical subject of a singular proposition, e.g., "the class of prime numbers comprises infinitely many objects". If we wanted to abrogate the law of excluded middle for the case of classes, we might then think of regarding classes—and in fact courses-of-values generally—as improper objects. These then would not be permitted to occur as arguments of all first-level functions. But there would also be functions that could take as arguments both proper and improper objects; certainly the relation of identity would be of this kind. We might try to escape this by assuming a special sort of identity for improper objects, but that is completely ruled out; identity is a relation given to us in so specific a form that it is inconceivable that various kinds of it should occur. But now there would result a great multiplicity of first-level functions, namely (1) those which could take only proper objects as arguments, (2) those which could take both proper and improper objects as arguments, and (3) those which could take only improper objects as arguments. There would also result another division on the basis of the values of functions, according to which we should have to distinguish (1) functions whose values were proper objects exclusively, (2) those which had both proper and improper objects as values, and (3) those whose values were improper objects exclusively. Both of these divisions of first-level functions would hold simultaneously, so that we should obtain nine types. To these again there would correspond nine types of courses-of-values, of improper objects, among which we should have to draw logical distinctions. Classes of proper objects would have to be distinguished from classes of classes of proper objects, extensions of relations between proper objects would have to be distinguished from classes of proper objects and from classes of extensions of relations between proper objects, and so on. Thus we should obtain an incalculable multiplicity of types; and in general objects belonging to different ones of these types could not occur as arguments of the same functions. But it seems extraordinarily difficult to set up comprehensive legislation that would decide in general which objects were permissible arguments for which functions. Moreover, the justifiability of the improper objects may be doubted.

If these difficulties frighten us off from regarding classes (and hence numbers) as improper objects, and if we are nonetheless unwilling to recognize them as proper objects, namely as admissible arguments for every first-level function, then there is indeed no alternative but to regard class-names as pseudo proper names, which would thus in fact have no denotation. They would in this case have to be regarded as parts of signs that had denotation only as wholes. [2] Now of course it may be thought advantageous for some purpose to fashion different signs that are identical in some part, without thereby making them into complex signs. The simplicity of a sign certainly requires only

255

---

[2] Cf. Vol. I, §29, pp. 84f., above.

that such parts as one can distinguish within it not have a denotation on their own. In this case, then, even what we are accustomed to regard as a sign for a number would not really be a sign at all, but a syncategorematic part of a sign. To define the sign "2" would be impossible; instead we should have to define many signs containing "2" as a syncategorematic constituent, but not construable as logical compounds of "2" and some other part. It would then be illicit to replace such a syncategorematic part by a letter, for so far as the content was concerned there would be no complexity. With this, the generality of arithmetical propositions would be lost. Again, it would be incomprehensible how on this basis we could speak of a Number of classes or a Number of Numbers.

I think that this is sufficient to render this route impassable as well. Thus there is no alternative at all but to recognize the extensions of concepts, or classes, as objects in the full and proper sense of the word, while conceding that our interpretation hitherto of the words "extension of a concept" is in need of justification.

Before we go into the matter more closely, it will be useful to track down the origin of this contradiction in our signs. That Δ is a class not belonging to itself may be expressed in this way:

$$\mathop{\rule[0.5ex]{0pt}{0pt}}\limits \; \grave{\epsilon}\left(\underline{\quad} \, {\it g}(\epsilon)\right) = \Delta .$$

And the class of classes not belonging to themselves will be designated thus:

$$\grave{\epsilon}\left(\mathop{\rule[0.5ex]{0pt}{0pt}}\limits \; \grave{\epsilon}\left(\underline{\quad} \, {\it g}(\epsilon)\right) = \epsilon\right)^{3}.$$

I shall use the sign "$\mathbf{V}$" as short for this in the derivation that follows, and in consideration of the doubtful truth of it all I shall omit the judgment-stroke. Accordingly, by

$$\text{``}\mathop{\rule[0.5ex]{0pt}{0pt}}\limits \; \grave{\epsilon}\left(\underline{\quad} \, {\it g}(\epsilon)\right) = \mathbf{V}\text{''}$$

I shall express the circumstance of the class $\mathbf{V}$'s not belonging to itself.

By (Vb) we now have

---

[3] On the use of Greek letters, cf. Volume I, §9.

$$\left[\begin{array}{l}(—\!\!—\,f(\mathbf{V})) = \neg\!\!\begin{array}{l}\mathfrak{g}\\ \mathfrak{g}(\mathbf{V})\\ \dot\epsilon(—\!\!—\,\mathfrak{g}(\epsilon)) = \mathbf{V}\end{array}\\[1em] \dot\epsilon(—\!\!—\,f(\epsilon)) = \dot\epsilon\left(\neg\!\!\begin{array}{l}\mathfrak{g}\\ \mathfrak{g}(\epsilon)\\ \dot\epsilon(—\!\!—\,\mathfrak{g}(\epsilon)) = \epsilon\end{array}\right)\end{array}\right.$$

or, by our abbreviation and (IIIa),

$$\begin{array}{l}\left[\begin{array}{l}f(\mathbf{V})\\ \dot\epsilon(—\!\!—\,f(\epsilon)) = \mathbf{V}\end{array}\right.\\[1em] \neg\!\!\begin{array}{l}\mathfrak{g}\\ \mathfrak{g}(\mathbf{V})\\ \dot\epsilon(—\!\!—\,\mathfrak{g}(\epsilon)) = \mathbf{V}\end{array}\,.\end{array} \qquad (a$$

Now for "f" we introduce the Gothic "$\mathfrak{g}$":

$$\begin{array}{l}\left[\begin{array}{l}\mathfrak{g}\\ \mathfrak{g}(\mathbf{V})\\ \dot\epsilon(—\!\!—\,\mathfrak{g}(\epsilon)) = \mathbf{V}\end{array}\right.\\[1em] \neg\!\!\begin{array}{l}\mathfrak{g}\\ \mathfrak{g}(\mathbf{V})\\ \dot\epsilon(—\!\!—\,\mathfrak{g}(\epsilon)) = \mathbf{V}\end{array}\,;\end{array} \qquad (\beta$$

i.e., if $\mathbf{V}$ does not belong to itself then $\mathbf{V}$ does belong to itself. That is one side.

On the other side, by (IIb) we have

$$\begin{array}{l}\left[\begin{array}{l}f(\mathbf{V})\\ \dot\epsilon(—\!\!—\,f(\epsilon)) = \mathbf{V}\end{array}\right.\\[1em] \neg\!\!\begin{array}{l}\mathfrak{g}\\ \mathfrak{g}(\mathbf{V})\\ \dot\epsilon(—\!\!—\,\mathfrak{g}(\epsilon)) = \mathbf{V}\end{array}\,,\end{array} \qquad (\gamma$$

and if for "$f(\xi)$" we take "$\neg\!\!\begin{array}{l}\mathfrak{g}\\ \mathfrak{g}(\xi)\\ \dot\epsilon(—\!\!—\,\mathfrak{g}(\epsilon)) = \xi\end{array}$",

$$\begin{array}{l}\left[\begin{array}{l}\neg\!\!\begin{array}{l}\mathfrak{g}\\ \mathfrak{g}(\mathbf{V})\\ \dot\epsilon(—\!\!—\,\mathfrak{g}(\epsilon)) = \mathbf{V}\end{array}\\[1em] \dot\epsilon\left(\neg\!\!\begin{array}{l}\mathfrak{g}\\ \mathfrak{g}(\epsilon)\\ \dot\epsilon(—\!\!—\,\mathfrak{g}(\epsilon)) = \epsilon\end{array}\right) = \mathbf{V}\end{array}\right.\\[2em] \neg\!\!\begin{array}{l}\mathfrak{g}\\ \mathfrak{g}(\mathbf{V})\\ \dot\epsilon(—\!\!—\,\mathfrak{g}(\epsilon)) = \mathbf{V}\end{array}\,,\end{array} \qquad (\delta$$

whence, taking into account our abbreviation,

$$\begin{array}{l}\left[\begin{array}{l}\neg\!\!\begin{array}{l}\mathfrak{g}\\ \mathfrak{g}(\mathbf{V})\\ \dot\epsilon(—\!\!—\,\mathfrak{g}(\epsilon)) = \mathbf{V}\end{array}\end{array}\right.\\[1em] \neg\!\!\begin{array}{l}\mathfrak{g}\\ \mathfrak{g}(\mathbf{V})\\ \dot\epsilon(—\!\!—\,\mathfrak{g}(\epsilon)) = \mathbf{V}\end{array}\,;\end{array} \qquad (\epsilon$$

i.e., if $\mathbf{V}$ belongs to itself then it does not belong to itself. From (ϵ) there follows by (Ig)

$$\neg\!\!\begin{array}{l}\mathfrak{g}\\ \mathfrak{g}(\mathbf{V})\\ \dot\epsilon(—\!\!—\,\mathfrak{g}(\epsilon)) = \mathbf{V}\end{array} \qquad (\zeta$$

and from this and (β),

$$\begin{array}{l} \raise2pt\hbox{$\!-\!\mathcal{I}\!$}\\[-4pt] \rule{0pt}{0pt}\quad\llap{L}{}_{\displaystyle \mathfrak{g}(\mathbf{V})}\\[2pt] \rule{0pt}{0pt}\qquad \grave{\epsilon}(\underline{\quad}\,{}_{\mathfrak{g}(\epsilon)}) = \mathbf{V}. \end{array} \qquad (\eta$$

The propositions (ζ) and (η) contradict one another. The error can be only in our Law (Vb), which must therefore be false.

Now let us see how the matter turns out if we make use of our sign "$\cap$". Here "$\grave{\epsilon}(\underline{\top}\,\epsilon\cap\epsilon)$" will occur in place of "$\mathbf{V}$". If in our proposition (82)* we take

$$\begin{array}{ccc} \text{``}\underline{\top}\,\xi\cap\xi\text{''} & \quad\text{for}\quad & \text{``}f(\xi)\text{''},\\[4pt] \text{``}\underline{\quad}\,\xi\text{''} & \quad\text{for}\quad & \text{``}F(\xi)\text{''},\\[4pt] \text{and ``}\grave{\epsilon}(\underline{\top}\,\epsilon\cap\epsilon)\text{''} & \quad\text{for}\quad & \text{``}a\text{''}, \end{array}$$

then we obtain

$$\begin{array}{l} \llap{L}\,\grave{\epsilon}(\underline{\top}\,\epsilon\cap\epsilon)\cap\grave{\epsilon}(\underline{\top}\,\epsilon\cap\epsilon)\\[4pt] \quad\grave{\epsilon}(\underline{\top}\,\epsilon\cap\epsilon)\cap\grave{\epsilon}(\underline{\top}\,\epsilon\cap\epsilon)\,, \end{array} \qquad (\theta$$

from which by (Ig) there follows

$$\underline{\top}\,\grave{\epsilon}(\underline{\top}\,\epsilon\cap\epsilon)\cap\grave{\epsilon}(\underline{\top}\,\epsilon\cap\epsilon)\,. \qquad (\iota$$

Making the same substitutions in proposition (77)*, we obtain

$$\begin{array}{l} \llap{L}\,\grave{\epsilon}(\underline{\top}\,\epsilon\cap\epsilon)\cap\grave{\epsilon}(\underline{\top}\,\epsilon\cap\epsilon)\\[4pt] \quad\grave{\epsilon}(\underline{\top}\,\epsilon\cap\epsilon)\cap\grave{\epsilon}(\underline{\top}\,\epsilon\cap\epsilon)\,, \end{array} \qquad (\kappa$$

from which together with (ι) there follows

$$\underline{\quad}\,\grave{\epsilon}(\underline{\top}\,\epsilon\cap\epsilon)\cap\grave{\epsilon}(\underline{\top}\,\epsilon\cap\epsilon)\,, \qquad (\lambda$$

which contradicts (ι). Therefore at least one of the two propositions (77) and (82) must be false, and therefore proposition (1) also, from which they both follow. A look at the derivation of (1) in §55 of our first volume** shows that there too use is made of (Vb). Thus suspicion is directed at this proposition here as well.

Along with (Vb), (V) itself has collapsed, but not (Va). Nothing hinders us from transforming the generality of an identity into an identity of courses-of-values; only the converse transformation has been shown to be not always allowable. Of course from this we learn that my way of introducing courses-of-values in §3 of Volume I*** is not always legitimate. We can *not* use the words:

"the function $\Phi(\xi)$ has the same course-of-values as the function $\Psi(\xi)$"

generally to denote the same as the words:

"the functions $\Phi(\xi)$ and $\Psi(\xi)$ have always the same value for the same argument",

and we must take into account the possibility that there are

---

*Cf. Appendix I, p. 126, above.

**Cf. Appendix I, pp. 123-125, above.

***Cf. p. 36, above.

concepts having no extension—at any rate, none in the ordinary sense of the word. Because of this, the justification of our second-level function $\dot{\epsilon}\phi(\epsilon)$ is shaken; yet such a function is indispensable for laying the foundation of arithmetic.

Now we shall supplement our inquiry by arriving at the falsehood of (Vb) as the end result of a derivation, instead of starting with (Vb) and thus running into a contradiction. In order to be independent of the signs for courses-of-values, which are after all under suspicion, we shall carry out the derivation quite generally for a second-level function of one argument of type 2,[4] using the notation of Volume I, §25. Our complex sign

$$``\dot{\epsilon}\left(\overset{\mathcal{g}}{\underset{\dot{\epsilon}(}{\rule{0pt}{1em}}}\!\!\!\frac{\mathcal{g}(\epsilon)}{\quad\ \ g(\epsilon)) = \epsilon}\right)\text{''}$$

258 will accordingly be replaced by

$$``M_\beta\left(\overset{\mathcal{g}}{\underset{M_\beta(}{\rule{0pt}{1em}}}\!\!\!\frac{\mathcal{g}(\beta)}{\quad\ \ g(\beta)) = \beta}\right)\text{''}\ ;$$

the stipulations that we set up in Volume I, §9, for the case of courses-of-values-signs regarding the scope of a Greek letter are to be carried over to this case as appropriate for the meaning. In our formula are two occurrences of "M", one initially and one in the interior. In the first occurrence what stands at the argument-place is the function-mark

$$``\overset{\mathcal{g}}{\underset{M_\beta(}{\rule{0pt}{1em}}}\!\!\!\frac{\mathcal{g}(\xi)}{\quad\ \ g(\beta)) = \xi}\text{''}\ ;$$

in the second occurrence it is "$\underline{\quad}g(\xi)$". The following at once results:

IIb*

$$\begin{aligned}&\overset{\mathcal{g}}{\underset{M_\beta(}{\rule{0pt}{1em}}}\frac{g(a)}{\quad g(\beta)) = a}\\&\quad M_\beta\left(\overset{\mathcal{g}}{\underset{M_\beta(}{\rule{0pt}{1em}}}\frac{g(\beta)}{\quad g(\beta)) = \beta}\right) = a\\&\overset{\mathcal{g}}{\underset{M_\beta(}{\rule{0pt}{1em}}}\frac{g(a)}{\quad g(\beta)) = a}\end{aligned}$$

$$\times$$

_____

[4] Cf. Volume I, §23, pp. 77–78, above.

*Frege is citing (IIb) in the form "$\begin{aligned}&M_\beta f(\beta)\\ \mathcal{g}\ &M_\beta g(\beta)\end{aligned}$",

for "$M_\beta(\phi(\beta))$" putting "$\underset{M_\beta(}{\rule{0pt}{1em}}\frac{\phi(a)}{\quad\ \phi(\beta)) = a}$",

and for "$f(\xi)$" putting "$\overset{\mathcal{g}}{\underset{M_\beta(}{\rule{0pt}{1em}}}\frac{g(\xi)}{\quad\ g(\beta)) = \xi}$".

$$\vdash \begin{array}{l} M_\beta\!\left(\begin{array}{l} \multimap \mathfrak{g}(\beta) \\ M_\beta(\text{---}\,\mathfrak{g}(\beta)) = \beta \end{array}\right) = a \\[4pt] \mathfrak{g}(a) \\ M_\beta(\text{---}\,\mathfrak{g}(\beta)) = a \end{array} \qquad (\mu$$

$$\times$$

$$\vdash \begin{array}{l} \multimap \mathfrak{g}(a) \\ M_\beta(\text{---}\,\mathfrak{g}(\beta)) = a \\[4pt] M_\beta\!\left(\begin{array}{l} \multimap \mathfrak{g}(\beta) \\ M_\beta(\text{---}\,\mathfrak{g}(\beta)) = \beta \end{array}\right) = a \end{array} \qquad (\nu$$

If for short we put

$$\text{``}\Phi(\xi)\text{''} \qquad \text{for} \qquad \text{``}\begin{array}{l} \multimap \mathfrak{g}(\xi) \\ M_\beta(\text{---}\,\mathfrak{g}(\beta)) = \xi \end{array}\text{''}$$

and

$$\text{``}M_\beta \Phi(\beta)\text{''} \qquad \text{for} \qquad \text{``}a\text{''},$$

then from (ν) we obtain

$$\Phi(M_\beta(\Phi(\beta)))\,;$$

i.e., the value of our second-level function for the concept $\Phi(\xi)$ as argument falls under this very concept. On the other hand, by (ν) we also have

$$\begin{array}{l} \multimap \mathfrak{g}(M_\beta(\Phi(\beta))) \\ M_\beta(\text{---}\,\mathfrak{g}(\beta)) = M_\beta(\Phi(\beta))\,, \end{array}$$

i.e., there is a concept which when taken as argument of our second-level function results in the same value as results when $\Phi(\xi)$ is so taken—but under which this value does not fall. In other words: for every second-level function of one argument of type 2 there are two concepts such that, taken as arguments of this function, they determine the same value, but also such that this value does fall under the first concept and does not fall 259 under the second.

This may be derived in Begriffsschrift as follows:

$$\nu \quad \vdash \begin{array}{l} \multimap \mathfrak{g}(a) \\ M_\beta(\text{---}\,\mathfrak{g}(\beta)) = a \\[4pt] M_\beta\!\left(\begin{array}{l} \multimap \mathfrak{g}(\beta) \\ M_\beta(\text{---}\,\mathfrak{g}(\beta)) = \beta \end{array}\right) = a \end{array}$$

(IIIa): ―――――――――――――――――

134

$$\left[\begin{array}{l} f(a) \\ M_\beta \left(\begin{array}{l} g(\beta) \\ M_\beta(\underline{\quad} g(\beta)) = \beta \end{array} \right) = a \end{array} \right.$$

$$\left[\begin{array}{l} f(a) = g(a) \\ \quad M_\beta(\underline{\quad} g(\beta)) = a \end{array} \right. \qquad (\xi$$

(IIb):: — — — — — — — — — — — — — — — —

$$\left[\begin{array}{l} f(a) \\ M_\beta \left(\begin{array}{l} g(\beta) \\ M_\beta(\underline{\quad} g(\beta)) = \beta \end{array} \right) = a \\ M_\beta(\underline{\quad} f(\beta)) = M_\beta \left(\begin{array}{l} g(\beta) \\ M_\beta(\underline{\quad} g(\beta)) = \beta \end{array} \right) \end{array} \right.$$

$$\mathcal{F} \left[\begin{array}{l} \mathcal{F}(a) = g(a) \\ \quad M_\beta(\underline{\quad} g(\beta)) = a \\ M_\beta(\underline{\quad} \mathcal{F}(\beta)) = M_\beta \left(\begin{array}{l} g(\beta) \\ M_\beta(\underline{\quad} g(\beta)) = \beta \end{array} \right) \end{array} \right. \qquad (\text{o}$$

(IIb, IIIa):: =

$$\left[\begin{array}{l} f(a) \\ M_\beta(\underline{\quad} f(\beta)) = a \\ M_\beta \left(\begin{array}{l} g(\beta) \\ M_\beta(\underline{\quad} g(\beta)) = \beta \end{array} \right) = a \end{array} \right.$$

$$\mathcal{G} \ \mathcal{F} \left[\begin{array}{l} \mathcal{F}(a) = \mathcal{G}(a) \\ M_\beta(\underline{\quad} \mathcal{F}(\beta)) = M_\beta(\underline{\quad} \mathcal{G}(\beta)) \end{array} \right. \qquad (\pi$$

$$\left[\begin{array}{l} g(a) \\ M_\beta(\underline{\quad} g(\beta)) = a \\ M_\beta \left(\begin{array}{l} g(\beta) \\ M_\beta(\underline{\quad} g(\beta)) = \beta \end{array} \right) = a \end{array} \right.$$

$$\mathcal{G} \ \mathcal{F} \left[\begin{array}{l} \mathcal{F}(a) = \mathcal{G}(a) \\ M_\beta(\underline{\quad} \mathcal{F}(\beta)) = M_\beta(\underline{\quad} \mathcal{G}(\beta)) \end{array} \right. \qquad (\rho$$

(μ): — — — — — — — — — — — — — — — — — —

135

$$M_\beta\left(\mathop{\rightharpoonup}\limits^{\mathfrak{g}} \begin{array}{l} \mathfrak{g}(\beta) \\ M_\beta(\!\!-\!\!-\mathfrak{g}(\beta)) = \beta \end{array}\right) = a$$

$$M_\beta\left(\mathop{\rightharpoonup}\limits^{\mathfrak{g}} \begin{array}{l} \mathfrak{g}(\beta) \\ M_\beta(\!\!-\!\!-\mathfrak{g}(\beta)) = \beta \end{array}\right) = a$$

$$\mathcal{G}\ \mathcal{F}\ \begin{array}{l} \mathcal{F}(a) = \mathcal{G}(a) \\ M_\beta(\!\!-\!\!-\mathcal{F}(\beta)) = M_\beta(\!\!-\!\!-\mathcal{G}(\beta)) \end{array}$$ $(\sigma$

(Ig): — — — — — — — — — — — — — — — — — — —

$$M_\beta\left(\mathop{\rightharpoonup}\limits^{\mathfrak{g}} \begin{array}{l} \mathfrak{g}(\beta) \\ M_\beta(\!\!-\!\!-\mathfrak{g}(\beta)) = \beta \end{array}\right) = a$$

$$\mathcal{G}\ \mathcal{F}\ \begin{array}{l} \mathcal{F}(a) = \mathcal{G}(a) \\ M_\beta(\!\!-\!\!-\mathcal{F}(\beta)) = M_\beta(\!\!-\!\!-\mathcal{G}(\beta)) \end{array}$$ $(\tau$

(IIa):: — — — — — — — — — — — — — — — — — —

$$M_\beta\left(\mathop{\rightharpoonup}\limits^{\mathfrak{g}} \begin{array}{l} \mathfrak{g}(\beta) \\ M_\beta(\!\!-\!\!-\mathfrak{g}(\beta)) = \beta \end{array}\right) = a$$

$$a\ \mathcal{G}\ \mathcal{F}\ \begin{array}{l} \mathcal{F}(a) = \mathcal{G}(a) \\ M_\beta(\!\!-\!\!-\mathcal{F}(\beta)) = M_\beta(\!\!-\!\!-\mathcal{G}(\beta)) \end{array}$$ $(\upsilon$

$$\times$$

$$a\ \mathcal{G}\ \mathcal{F}\ \begin{array}{l} \mathcal{F}(a) = \mathcal{G}(a) \\ M_\beta(\!\!-\!\!-\mathcal{F}(\beta)) = M_\beta(\!\!-\!\!-\mathcal{G}(\beta)) \end{array}$$

$$M_\beta\left(\mathop{\rightharpoonup}\limits^{\mathfrak{g}} \begin{array}{l} \mathfrak{g}(\beta) \\ M_\beta(\!\!-\!\!-\mathfrak{g}(\beta)) = \beta \end{array}\right) = a$$ $(\phi$

— • —

(IIIe) $\vdash M_\beta\left(\mathop{\rightharpoonup}\limits^{\mathfrak{g}} \begin{array}{l} \mathfrak{g}(\beta) \\ M_\beta(\!\!-\!\!-\mathfrak{g}(\beta)) = \beta \end{array}\right) = M_\beta\left(\mathop{\rightharpoonup}\limits^{\mathfrak{g}} \begin{array}{l} \mathfrak{g}(\beta) \\ M_\beta(\!\!-\!\!-\mathfrak{g}(\beta)) = \beta \end{array}\right)$

(ϕ): ————————————————————————

$$a\ \mathcal{G}\ \mathcal{F}\ \begin{array}{l} \mathcal{F}(a) = \mathcal{G}(a) \\ M_\beta(\!\!-\!\!-\mathcal{F}(\beta)) = M_\beta(\!\!-\!\!-\mathcal{G}(\beta)) \end{array}$$ $(\chi$

That is, for every second-level function of one argument of type 2 there are concepts which if taken as arguments of this function determine the same value, although not all objects falling under one of these concepts also fall under the other.

Our proof has been carried out without the use of propositions or notations whose justification is in any way doubtful. Our proposition thus holds good for the second-level function $\acute{e}\phi(\epsilon)$, supposing this to be legitimate; or, in words: If it is permissible generally for any first-level concept that we speak of its extension, then the case arises of concepts' having the same extension although not all objects falling under one also fall under the other.

However, this simply does away with extensions of concepts in the received sense of the term. We may not say that in general the expression

> "the extension of one concept coincides with that of another"

denotes the same as the expression

> "every object falling under the first concept also falls under the second, and conversely".

From the result of our derivation we see that it simply is not possible to connect with the words "the extension of the concept $\Phi(\xi)$" such a sense that in general from identity of extension of two concepts we could infer that every object falling under one of them also fell under the other.

Our proposition can also be reached in another way, namely as follows:

IIb

$$M_\beta\left(\overset{\mathfrak{g}}{}\mathfrak{g}(a),\; M_\beta(\text{—}\,\mathfrak{g}(\beta)) = a\right)$$
$$M_\beta\left(\overset{\mathfrak{g}}{}\mathfrak{g}(\beta),\; M_\beta(\text{—}\,\mathfrak{g}(\beta)) = \beta\right) = a$$
$$\overset{\mathfrak{g}}{}\mathfrak{g}(a),\; M_\beta(\text{—}\,\mathfrak{g}(\beta)) = a$$

$$\times$$

$$M_\beta\left(\overset{\mathfrak{g}}{}\mathfrak{g}(\beta),\; M_\beta(\text{—}\,\mathfrak{g}(\beta)) = \beta\right) = a$$
$$\overset{\mathfrak{g}}{}\mathfrak{g}(a),\; M_\beta(\text{—}\,\mathfrak{g}(\beta)) = a \qquad (\psi$$

$$\times$$

$$\overset{\mathfrak{g}}{}\mathfrak{g}(a),\; M_\beta(\text{—}\,\mathfrak{g}(\beta)) = a$$
$$M_\beta\left(\overset{\mathfrak{g}}{}\mathfrak{g}(\beta),\; M_\beta(\text{—}\,\mathfrak{g}(\beta)) = \beta\right) = a \qquad (\omega$$

137

If for short here we put "$\Psi(\xi)$" for

$$\text{``} \overset{\mathfrak{s}}{\underset{\beta}{\bigsqcup}} \begin{array}{l} \mathfrak{q}(\xi) \\ M_\beta(\underline{\quad} \mathfrak{q}(\beta) = \xi \end{array} \text{''}$$

and replace "a" by "$M_\beta(\Psi(\beta))$", then from (ω) we obtain

$$\underline{\quad} \Psi(M_\beta(\Psi(\beta)))\,;$$

i.e., the value of our second-level function for the argument $\Psi(\xi)$ does not itself fall under the concept $\Psi(\xi)$. On the other hand, from (ω) we also have

$$\overset{\mathfrak{s}}{\underset{\beta}{\bigsqcup}} \begin{array}{l} \mathfrak{q}(M_\beta(\Psi(\beta))) \\ M_\beta(\underline{\quad} \mathfrak{q}(\beta)) = M_\beta(\Psi(\beta))\,; \end{array}$$

i.e., there is a concept which, when taken as argument of our second-level function, results in the same value as results when $\Psi(\xi)$ is so taken—and under which this value does fall. Thus here too, we have two concepts which, taken as arguments of the second-level function, determine the same value, where yet the value does fall under the second concept, but not under the first. We can derive the proposition (χ) from (ω) in a way similar to 262 our derivation of it from (ν).

Now let us try taking the function $\acute{\epsilon}(\underline{\quad} \phi(\epsilon))$ as the second-level function referred to in our foregoing propositions. We then have in the concept

$$\overset{\mathfrak{s}}{\underset{}{\bigsqcup}} \begin{array}{l} \mathfrak{q}(\xi) \\ \acute{\epsilon}(\underline{\quad} \mathfrak{q}(\epsilon)) = \xi \end{array}$$

a concept under which its own extension falls; but by (ν) there is a concept whose extension coincides with that of the concept just mentioned, but under which this extension does not fall. We should like to have an example of this: how is such a concept to be found? It cannot be done without a more precise specification of our function $\acute{\epsilon}(\underline{\quad} \phi(\epsilon))$, of the extension of a concept; for our previous criterion for the coinciding of extensions at this point forsakes us.

On the other hand, we have in the concept

$$\overset{\mathfrak{s}}{\underset{}{\bigsqcup}} \begin{array}{l} \mathfrak{q}(\xi) \\ \acute{\epsilon}(\underline{\quad} \mathfrak{q}(\epsilon)) = \xi \end{array}$$

a concept under which its extension does not fall; but by (ω) there is a concept whose extension coincides with that of the concept just mentioned, under which this extension does fall—all

138

of this naturally on the hypothesis that the function-name "$\acute{\epsilon}(\underline{\quad}\,\phi(\epsilon))$" has a logical justification.

In both cases we see that the exceptional case is constituted by the extension itself, in that it falls under only one of two concepts whose extension it is; and we see that the occurrence of this exception can in no way be avoided. Accordingly the following suggests itself as criterion of identity for extensions: the extension of one concept coincides with that of another if every object that falls under the first concept, except the extension of the first concept, also falls under the extension of the second concept, and if conversely every object that falls under the second concept, except the extension of the second concept, also falls under the first concept.*

Obviously this cannot be taken as *defining* the extension of a concept, but merely as stating the distinctive property of this second-level function.

By transferring to courses-of-values in general what we have said of extensions of concepts, we arrive at the Basic Law

$$\vdash (\acute{\epsilon} f(\epsilon) = \acute{\alpha} g(a)) = \overset{a}{\underset{}{\rule{0pt}{0pt}}}\!\!\begin{array}{l} f(a) = g(a) \\ a = \acute{\epsilon} f(\epsilon) \\ a = \acute{\alpha} g(a) \end{array} \qquad (V')$$

which is to replace (V) (Volume I, §20, p. 72, above). This Law implies (Va). On the other hand, (Vb) must give way to the following propositions:

$$\begin{array}{l} f(a) = g(a) \\ a = \acute{\epsilon} f(\epsilon) \\ \acute{\epsilon} f(\epsilon) = \acute{\alpha} g(a) \end{array} \qquad (V'b)$$

or

$$\begin{array}{l} f(a) = g(a) \\ a = \acute{\alpha} g(a) \\ \acute{\epsilon} f(\epsilon) = \acute{\alpha} g(a) \end{array} \qquad (V'c)$$

Let us now convince ourselves that the contradiction that arose earlier between the propositions (β) and (ϵ) is now avoided. We proceed as we did in the derivation of (β), using (V'c) instead of (Vb). As before, let "$\mathbf{V}$" abbreviate

263

---

*This suggestion is now known not to be far-reaching enough to eliminate inconsistency from the system; see the Editor's Introduction, pp. xlvff., and the articles there cited.

$$\text{``}\grave{\epsilon}\left(\underset{\grave{\epsilon}(\underline{\quad}\,g(\epsilon))\,=\,\epsilon}{\overset{g}{\rule{0pt}{1em}}}\,g(\epsilon)\right)\text{''}.$$

By (V′c) we have

$$\begin{array}{l}
(\underline{\quad}\,f(\mathbf{V})) = \underset{\grave{\epsilon}(\underline{\quad}\,g(\epsilon))\,=\,\mathbf{V}}{\overset{g}{\rule{0pt}{1em}}}\,g(\mathbf{V})\\[2pt]
\mathbf{V} = \grave{\epsilon}\left(\underset{\grave{\epsilon}(\underline{\quad}\,g(\epsilon))\,=\,\epsilon}{\overset{g}{\rule{0pt}{1em}}}\,g(\epsilon)\right)\\[2pt]
\grave{\epsilon}(\underline{\quad}\,f(\epsilon)) = \grave{\epsilon}\left(\underset{\grave{\epsilon}(\underline{\quad}\,g(\epsilon))\,=\,\epsilon}{\overset{g}{\rule{0pt}{1em}}}\,g(\epsilon)\right).
\end{array}$$

Using our abbreviation, we obtain

$$\begin{array}{l}
(\underline{\quad}\,f(\mathbf{V}) = \underset{\grave{\epsilon}(\underline{\quad}\,g(\epsilon))\,=\,\mathbf{V}}{\overset{g}{\rule{0pt}{1em}}}\,g(\mathbf{V})\\[2pt]
\mathbf{V} = \mathbf{V}\\[2pt]
\grave{\epsilon}(\underline{\quad}\,f(\epsilon)) = \grave{\epsilon}\left(\underset{\grave{\epsilon}(\underline{\quad}\,g(\epsilon))\,=\,\epsilon}{\overset{g}{\rule{0pt}{1em}}}\,g(\epsilon)\right),
\end{array}$$

which is obviously true because of the subcomponent "$\underline{\quad}\mathbf{V} = \mathbf{V}$", and on that very account can never lead to a contradiction.

We stipulated (Volume I, p. 48, above) that the extension of a concept under which falls only the True should be the True, and that the extension of a concept under which falls only the False should be the False. These specifications remain unchanged by our new understanding of the extensions of concepts.

What influence does this new interpretation have upon the values of our function $\backslash\xi$, if we hold to the specifications of Volume I, §11 [pp. 49-50, above]? Suppose $\Phi(\xi)$ is an empty concept; by the old interpretation of extensions, $\backslash\grave{\epsilon}\,\Phi(\epsilon)$ then coincided with $\grave{\epsilon}\,\Phi(\epsilon)$, because there was no object Δ such that $\grave{\epsilon}(\Delta = \epsilon)$ coincided with $\grave{\epsilon}\,\Phi(\epsilon)$. By the new interpretation there is such an object, viz., $\grave{\epsilon}\,\Phi(\epsilon)$ itself. But the result is again the same, viz., that $\backslash\grave{\epsilon}\,\Phi(\epsilon)$ coincides with $\grave{\epsilon}\,\Phi(\epsilon)$. Similarly if $\grave{\epsilon}\,\Phi(\epsilon)$ is the sole object falling under the concept $\Phi(\xi)$. If we assume Δ to be the sole object falling under the concept $\Phi(\xi)$, then $\backslash\grave{\epsilon}\,\Phi(\epsilon)$ coincides with Δ. This is also the case if only Δ and $\grave{\epsilon}\,\Phi(\epsilon)$ fall under the concept $\Phi(\xi)$; and here the case is different from before, for in this case $\backslash\grave{\epsilon}\,\Phi(\epsilon)$ was before supposed to coincide not with Δ but with $\grave{\epsilon}\,\Phi(\epsilon)$. In all other cases there is no difference between the old and the new interpretation of the extensions of concepts as regards the values of the function $\backslash\xi$, and our Basic Law (VI) holds now as it did earlier.

We have yet to ask how the values of our function $\xi \cap \zeta$ are affected by the new interpretation of courses-of-values. Where Γ is a course-of-values, it is no longer specified what value a function has, whose course-of-values is Γ, for the argument Θ;[5] in particular: when Θ coincides with Γ. There can be functions having the same course-of-values Γ, but having different values for the argument Γ. The extension of the concept

$$-\!\!\!\curvearrowleft\!\!\top\!\!\begin{array}{l} g(\Gamma) = \xi \\ \Gamma = \acute{\epsilon} g(\epsilon) \end{array}$$

can now no longer coincide with the extension of a concept like $\Delta = \xi$, because Δ alone falls under the latter, whereas all objects fall under the former. For, if Γ is a course-of-values and E is an object, it is always possible to specify a function $X(\xi)$ such that

$$\acute{\epsilon} X(\epsilon) = \Gamma \quad \text{and}$$
$$X(\Gamma) = E .$$

By the stipulation of Volume I, §11,

$$\grave{\mathfrak{a}} \left(-\!\!\!\curvearrowleft\!\!\top\!\!\begin{array}{l} g(\Gamma) = \mathfrak{a} \\ \Gamma = \acute{\epsilon} g(\epsilon) \end{array} \right)$$

accordingly coincides with

$$\grave{\mathfrak{a}} \left(-\!\!\!\curvearrowleft\!\!\top\!\!\begin{array}{l} g(\Gamma) = \mathfrak{a} \\ \Gamma = \acute{\epsilon} g(\epsilon) \end{array} \right) .$$

Thus if Γ is a course-of-values, then

$$\Gamma \cap \Gamma = \grave{\mathfrak{a}} \left(-\!\!\!\curvearrowleft\!\!\top\!\!\begin{array}{l} g(\Gamma) = \mathfrak{a} \\ \Gamma = \acute{\epsilon} g(\epsilon) \end{array} \right)$$

[is the True]; i.e., $\Gamma \cap \Gamma$ is the extension of a concept that encompasses everything. If Γ is not a course-of-values, then $\Gamma \cap \Gamma$ is the extension of an empty concept. In the first case $-\!\!\!-\Gamma \cap \Gamma$ is the False:

$$\vdash \acute{\epsilon} f(\epsilon) \cap \acute{\epsilon} f(\epsilon) . \qquad\qquad (a'$$

This is important for the function $\mathscr{D}\xi$. At first sight we might be apprehensive that concepts having the same extension would by our stipulations have to be assigned the same Number, even though one more object fell under the one than under the other— namely, the extension itself, so that in the end we should get only a single finite Number. However, to $\mathscr{D}\acute{\epsilon}\Phi(\epsilon)$ only the concept $-\!\!\!-\xi \cap \acute{\epsilon}\Phi(\epsilon)$ is relevant, and not the concept $\Phi(\xi)$, and the

---

[5] Cf. Volume I, pp. 92-93, above.

extension $\acute\epsilon\Phi(\epsilon)$ does not fall under the former, even if it does fall under $\Phi(\xi)$.

If we repeat the derivation of Theorem (1) (Volume I, §55)* with (V′b) instead of (Vb), then we obtain, instead of (1),

$$\vdash \begin{array}{l} f(a) = a \cap \acute\epsilon f(\epsilon) \\ a = \acute\epsilon f(\epsilon) \end{array} \tag{1′}$$

from which we derive, not (77) and (82), but

$$\vdash \begin{array}{l} F(a \cap \acute\epsilon f(\epsilon)) \\ F(f(a)) \\ a = \acute\epsilon f(\epsilon) \end{array} \tag{77′} \qquad \vdash \begin{array}{l} F(f(a)) \\ F(a \cap \acute\epsilon f(\epsilon)) \\ a = \acute\epsilon f(\epsilon) \end{array} \tag{82′}$$

We draw some additional consequences.

$$\text{(IIIa): } \dfrac{a' \quad \vdash \acute\epsilon f(\epsilon) \cap \acute\epsilon f(\epsilon)}{\vdash \begin{array}{l} a \cap \acute\epsilon f(\epsilon) \\ a = \acute\epsilon f(\epsilon) \end{array}} \tag{β'}$$

$$\text{(Ia): } -----\quad \vdash \begin{array}{l} f(a) \\ a \cap \acute\epsilon f(\epsilon) \\ a = \acute\epsilon f(\epsilon) \end{array}$$

$$\text{(82′): } \cdot - \cdot - \cdot - \cdot - \cdot \quad \vdash \begin{array}{l} f(a) \\ a \cap \acute\epsilon f(\epsilon) \end{array} \tag{82″}$$

$$\text{——} \bullet \text{——}$$

$$\text{(Ig): } \dfrac{82'' \quad \vdash \begin{array}{l} \acute\epsilon(\top \epsilon \cap \epsilon) \cap \acute\epsilon(\top \epsilon \cap \epsilon) \\ \acute\epsilon(\top \epsilon \cap \epsilon) \cap \acute\epsilon(\top \epsilon \cap \epsilon) \end{array}}{\vdash \acute\epsilon(\top \epsilon \cap \epsilon) \cap \acute\epsilon(\top \epsilon \cap \epsilon)} \tag{γ'}$$

This follows in the same way as (ι) above. Nonetheless no contradiction arises, as we shall immediately see. (γ') is merely a particular case of (a').

$$77' \quad \vdash \begin{array}{l} \acute\epsilon(\top \epsilon \cap \epsilon) \cap \acute\epsilon(\top \epsilon \cap \epsilon) \\ \acute\epsilon(\top \epsilon \cap \epsilon) \cap \acute\epsilon(\top \epsilon \cap \epsilon) \\ \acute\epsilon(\top \epsilon \cap \epsilon) = \acute\epsilon(\top \epsilon \cap \epsilon) \end{array}$$

$$\times$$

---

*Cf. Appendix I.

$$(\gamma')::\quad \dfrac{\begin{array}{l}\vdash \acute{\epsilon}(\tau\,\epsilon\cap\epsilon) = \acute{\epsilon}(\tau\,\epsilon\cap\epsilon) \\ \vdash \acute{\epsilon}(\tau\,\epsilon\cap\epsilon)\cap\acute{\epsilon}(\tau\,\epsilon\cap\epsilon)\end{array}}{\vdash \acute{\epsilon}(\tau\,\epsilon\cap\epsilon) = \acute{\epsilon}(\tau\,\epsilon\cap\epsilon)}\qquad\begin{array}{l}(\delta' \\[1.2em] (\epsilon'\end{array}$$

(ϵ') is a special case of (IIIe). A contradiction is not forthcoming.

To pursue further here the consequences of replacing (V) by (V′) would be too great an undertaking. We cannot but acknowledge that subcomponents must be added to many of the propositions; but certainly we need not fear that this will raise obstacles that actually block the course of the proofs. Nevertheless it will be necessary to check thoroughly all propositions discovered up to this point.

The prime problem of arithmetic is the question, In what way are we to conceive logical objects, in particular, numbers? By what means are we justified in recognizing numbers as objects? Even if this problem is not solved to the degree I thought it was when I wrote this volume, still I do not doubt that the way to the solution has been found.

Jena, October, 1902.

List of corrections and minor points not otherwise noted.

pp. 1-2. Although certain of the forward references refer to portions of the original book not included in this translation, the references have been included for the sake of the reader wishing to study the later portions in the original. The same applies to certain of the references at pp. 8-9.

p. 29. Paragraph §0 was called *"Einleitung"* in the original, the Introduction being called *"Vorwort"*.

p. 39, line 4. The original reads, "the function —— ξ" (instead of "the function-name "—— ξ" ").

p. 41, line 5. In the text, the right-hand side of the equation reads, "$x^2 - 1$".

p. 43, first four displayed formulas. In the text, instead of the last identity-sign in each of these there occur plus-signs.

p. 47, line 12. The original reads, "the function $\Phi(\xi)$" (instead of "some function $\Phi(\xi)$").

p. 47, line 7 from foot. The original reads, "$\Phi(\xi)$" (instead of "X(ξ)").

p. 51, line 5 from foot. The original reads, "the True" (instead of "the False"). The correction is given in *Grundgesetze*, vol. II, p. xvi.

p. 54, fourth display. In the original, "4" occurs in place of "3".

p. 55, beginning at line 18. Throughout the example the text has "—— 1" rather than "−1".

p. 58, line 6 from foot. In the text, the name "⊤Γ" is incorrectly written "⊢Γ".

p. 66, lines 13-14. The conclusion and one of the premisses are erroneously transposed in the text.

p. 96, line 16 from foot. The text has "ξ" instead of "ζ".

pp. 97-99. The capital upsilon not being available, a capital tau ("T") has been used instead. The same applies to pp. 102-104.

pp. 123-124. I have altered the indices in §54 to conform with those of §55.

p. 130, line 3 from foot. The original reads, "belonging" (instead of "not belonging").

p. 131, line 6. "Belongs" and "does not belong" are erroneously transposed in the text.

p. 131, line 3 from foot. "Belongs" and "does not belong" are erroneously transposed in the text.